*A Publication Distributed by Heron Books*

# *A Dickens Anthology*

CHARLES DICKENS
1812-1870

# *A Dickens Anthology*

*Selected and arranged by*
SIDNEY MACER-WRIGHT

*Illustrations by*
ELIZABETH ODLING

*Distributed by*
HERON BOOKS

*This book*
*is a production of*
*Heron Books, London*

*Printed and bound by*
*Hazell Watson & Viney Ltd,*
*Aylesbury, Bucks*

*Published by arrangement with*
*William Collins, Sons & Co. Ltd*

4103

# CONTENTS

## FOREWORD

When, over one hundred years ago, Dickens established his fame by writing The Posthumous Papers of the Pickwick Club there was no eight-hour day, there were no early closing days, there were no holidays whatever, excepting Christmas Day, for the majority of people and it was not until the year after his death that Bank Holidays were established; yet people found leisure time in which to read.

To-day there is leisure in abundance but it would sometimes seem that we have lost the ability to be leisurely; with the possession of motor cars and motor cycles, hours of restfulness have become hours of restlessness, and if the lack of these vehicles precludes one from rushing away in order to rush back again there is the wireless to distract the mind and television to rivet the attention to the exclusion of all else—even of one's friends and especially of those friends who so patiently wait on the book-shelf for a kindly nod of remembrance.

This little anthology, it is hoped, will give the opportunity to those who have so much leisure but so little time, those whose hours of ease are as overlaid with toil as are their working hours, of popping in upon the old friends to whom Dickens introduced them long ago and of saying, "Well, well, I'd almost forgotten you—I'll come again and read you right through once more." It may also, it is to be hoped, arouse the curiosity of those much to be envied young people who have yet to taste the delights of Dickens' novels and who, when they read them, will assuredly join with many of their elders in wishing there were still more to read.

When Pickwick Papers were being published in monthly parts people knew not how to wait for the next instalment. John Forster in his life of Dickens tells of a solemn clergyman who had been administering ghostly consolation to a sick person, and having finished satisfactorily, as he thought, and got out of the room, heard the sick man say, "Well, thank God, Pickwick will be out in ten days anyway."

John Forster also records that judges on the bench and boys in the street, gravity and folly, the young and the old, those who were entering life and those who were quitting it, alike found Pickwick irresistible. "Every class," he writes, "were attracted to it. The charm of its gaiety and good humour, its inexhaustible fun, its riotous overflow of animal spirits, its brightness and keenness of observation, and above all, the incomparable ease of its many varieties of enjoyment, fascinated everybody." And Dickens continues to be irresistible; judges on the bench and parsons in their pulpits, members in the Houses of Parliament and leader writers in the national press are constantly to be found quoting from his works to point a moral or adorn a tale.

It has been said that Dickens' characters are caricatures; that they are often fantastic, ridiculous, absurd. But to-day, as in Dickens' day, fantastic, absurd and ridiculous people abound everywhere—they still live, not only in his books but in the streets around us, and can easily be identified. Only their style of dress is changed. Despite the Welfare State there are still improvident and gloriously grandiloquent optimists waiting for something to turn up, and there must still be plenty of Mr. Dicks very much bemused by their own particular King Charles's head. There are, of course, some characters who have walked off the stage never to return, otherwise Dickens' reforming zeal would have gone for naught. Bumble may possibly have survived in some strange new disguise and lacking any semblance of power, but there are no ill-fed Oliver Twists left—if there be any well-fed ones with the audacity to "ask for more" they will certainly get it with the Government's blessing. Squeers likewise must have vanished with the passing of Dotheboys Hall, and if his unprepossessing daughter Fanny still survives she will at any rate not be so illiterate.

Scrooge no doubt continues to pursue his miserly tight-fisted way, but it is safe to assume that any Bob Cratchet foolish enough to work for him will be receiving proper wages and proper holidays. Mr. Pickwick should be easy to recognise—probably disporting himself on some country or seaside bowling green whilst Sam Weller is unquestionably to be found firing his witticisms at passengers and passers-by alike, from the conductor's platform of a city omnibus.

Dickens' womenfolk are perhaps not quite so easy to track down. Miss Betsy Trotwood, David Copperfield's endearing and strong-minded great aunt, should be found without much difficulty, although it is unlikely that she will be discovered waging war on trespassing donkeys. The tantalising Mrs. Varden and her flirtatious young daughter Dolly will be with us forever but the famous Sairey Gamp who attained such great eminence in her profession remains with us only as an immortal memory and will never again request that the bottle be left "on the chimley-piece, and let me put my lips to it when I am so dispoged."

Although Mrs. Gamp and Mr. Squeers and many another have gone forever, the world would certainly be a poorer place did the majority of Dickens' characters exist only within the pages of his books.

S.M-W.

# 1

# *The Philosophic Mind*

## THE DRONE PHILOSOPHY

Mr. Skimpole was as agreeable at breakfast, as he had been over-night. There was honey on the table, and it led him into a discourse about Bees. He had no objection to honey, he said (and I should think he had not, for he seemed to like it), but he protested against the overweening assumptions of Bees. He didn't at all see why the busy Bee should be proposed as a model to him; he supposed the Bee liked to make honey, or he wouldn't do it—nobody asked him. It was not necessary for the Bee to make such a merit of his tastes. If every confectioner went buzzing about the world, banging against every thing that came in his way, and egotistically calling upon everybody to take notice that he was going to his work and must not be interrupted, the world would be quite an unsupportable place. Then, after all, it was a ridiculous position, to be smoked out of your fortune with brimstone, as soon as you had made it. You would have a very mean opinion of a Manchester man, if he spun cotton for no other purpose. He must say he thought a Drone the embodiment of a pleasanter and wiser idea. The Drone said, unaffectedly, "You will excuse me; I really cannot attend to the shop! I find myself in a world in which there is so much to see, and so short a time to see it in, that I must take the liberty of looking about me, and begging to be provided for by somebody who doesn't want to look about him." This appeared to Mr. Skimpole to be the Drone philosophy, and he thought it a very good philosophy —always supposing the Drone to be willing to be on good terms with the Bee: which, so far as he knew, the easy fellow always was, if the consequential creature would only let him, and not be so conceited about his honey!

BLEAK HOUSE

## MRS. CHICK'S TOLERANCE

"We have all our faults," said Mrs. Chick, weeping and shaking her head. "I dare say we have. I never was blind to hers. I never said I was. Far from it. Yet how I loved her!"

What a satisfaction it was to Mrs. Chick, a commonplace piece of folly enough, compared with whom her sister-in-law had been a very angel of womanly intelligence and gentleness, to patronise and be tender to the memory of that lady—in exact persuance of her conduct to her in her lifetime—and to thoroughly believe herself, and take herself in, and make herself uncommonly comfortable on the strength of her toleration! What a mighty pleasant virtue toleration should be when we are right, to be so very pleasant when we are wrong, and quite unable to demonstrate how we come to be invested with the privilege of exercising it!

DOMBEY AND SON

## THE UPS AND DOWNS

Mr. Plornish amiably growled, in his philosophical but not lucid manner, that there was ups you see, and there was downs. It was in vain to ask why ups, why downs; there they was, you know. He had heerd it given for a truth that accordin' as the world went round, which round it did rewolve undoubted, even the best of gentlemen must take his turn of standing with his ed upside down and all his air a flying the wrong way into what you might call Space. Wery well then. What Mr. Plornish said was, wery well then. That gentleman's ed would come up'ards when his turn come, that gentleman's air would be a pleasure to look upon being all smooth again, and wery well then!

LITTLE DORRIT

## JOE GARGERY'S VIEW OF LIFE

"Pip, dear old chap, life is made up of ever so many partings welded together, as I may say, and one man's a blacksmith, and one's a whitesmith, and one's a goldsmith, and one's a coppersmith. Diwisions among such must come, and must be met as they come. If there's been any fault at all to-day, it's mine. You and me is not two figures to be together in London; nor yet anywheres else but what is private, and beknown, and understood among friends. It an't that I am proud, but that I want to be right, as you shall never see me no more in these clothes. I'm wrong in these clothes. I'm wrong out of the forge, the kitchen, or off the meshes. You won't find half so much fault in me if you think of me in my forge dress, with my hammer in my hand, or even my pipe. You won't find half so much fault in me if, supposing you should ever wish to see me, you come and put your head in at the forge window and see Joe, the blacksmith, there, at the old anvil, in the old burnt apron, sticking to the old work. I'm awful dull, but I hope I've beat out something nigh the rights of this at last. And so God bless you, dear old Pip, old chap, God bless you!"

GREAT EXPECTATIONS

## THE VOICE OF CONSCIENCE

"I am sure," said the gentleman, rubbing his forehead again, and drumming on the table as before, "I have good reason to believe that a jog-trot life, the same from day to day, would reconcile one to anything. One don't see anything, one don't hear anything, one don't know anything; that's the fact. We go on taking everything for granted, and so we go on, until whatever we do, good, bad, or indifferent, we do from habit. Habit is all I shall have to report when I am called upon to plead to my conscience on my death-bed. 'Habit,' says I; 'I was deaf, dumb, blind, and paralytic to a million things, from habit.' "Very business-like indeed, Mr. What's-your-name," says Conscience, "but it won't do here!"

DOMBEY AND SON

## THE HUMBUG OF THE BEE

". . . But there's nothing like work. Look at the bees."

"I beg your pardon," returned Eugene, with a reluctant smile, "but will you excuse my mentioning that I always protest against being referred to the bees?"

"Do you!" said Mr. Boffin.

"I object on principle," said Eugene, "as a biped——"

"As a what?" asked Mr. Boffin.

"As a two-footed creature;—I object on principle, as a two-footed creature, to being constantly referred to insects and four-footed creatures. I object to being required to model my proceedings according to the proceedings of the bee, or the dog, or the spider, or the camel. I fully admit that the camel, for instance, is an excessively temperate person; but he has several stomachs to entertain himself with, and I have only one. Besides, I am not fitted up with a convenient cool cellar to keep my drink in."

"But I said, you know," urged Mr. Boffin, rather at a loss for an answer, "the bee."

"Exactly. And may I represent to you that it's injudicious to say the bee? For the whole case is assumed. Conceding for a moment that there is any analogy between a bee and a man in a shirt and pantaloons (which I deny), and that it is settled that the man is to learn from the bee (which I also deny), the question still remains, What is he to learn? To imitate? Or to avoid? When your friends the bees worry themselves to that highly fluttered extent about their sovereign, and become perfectly distracted touching the slightest monarchical movement, are we men to learn the greatness of Tuft-hunting, or the littleness of the Court Circular? I am not clear, Mr. Boffin, but that the hive may be satirical."

"At all events, they work," said Mr. Boffin.

"Ye-es," returned Eugene, disparagingly, "they work; but don't you think they overdo it? They work so much more than they need—they make so much more than they can eat—they are so incessantly boring and buzzing at their one idea till Death comes upon them—that don't you think they overdo it? And are human labourers to have no holidays, because of the bees? And am I never to have change of air, because the bees don't? Mr. Boffin, I think honey excellent at breakfast; but regarded in the light of my conventional schoolmaster and moralist, I protest against the tyrannical humbug of your friend the bee. With the highest respect for you."

"Thankee," said Mr. Boffin. "Morning, morning!"

OUR MUTUAL FRIEND

# 2

# *A Bevy of Lovers*

## THE REPENTANT DOLLY VARDEN

. . . Dolly Varden came running into the room, in tears, threw herself on Joe's breast without a word of explanation, and clasped her white arms round his neck.

"Dolly!" cried Joe. "Dolly!"

"Ay, call me that—call me that always," exclaimed the locksmith's little daughter; "never speak coldly to me, never be distant, never again reprove me for the follies I have long repented, or I shall die, Joe."

"I reprove you!" said Joe.

"Yes—for every kind and honest word you uttered, went to my heart. For you, who have borne so much from me—for you, who owe your sufferings and pain to my caprice—for you to be so kind—so noble to me, Joe——"

He could say nothing to her—not a syllable. There was an odd sort of eloquence in his one arm, which had crept round her waist: but his lips were mute.

"If you had reminded me by a word—only by one short word," sobbed Dolly, clinging yet closer to him, "how little I deserved that you should treat me with so much forbearance; if you had exalted only for one moment in your triumph, I could have borne it better."

"Triumph!" repeated Joe, with a smile which seemed to say, "I am a pretty figure for that."

"Yes, triumph," she cried, with her whole heart and soul in her earnest voice, and gushing voice: "for it *is* one. I am glad to think and know it is. I wouldn't be less humbled, dear,—I wouldn't be without the recollection of that last time we spoke together in this place—no, not if I could recall the past, and make our parting yesterday."

Did ever lover look as Joe looked now!

"Dear Joe," said Dolly, "I always loved you—in my own heart I always did, although I was so vain and giddy, I hoped you would come back that night. I made quite sure you would. I prayed for it on my knees. Through all those long, long years, I have never once forgotten you, or left off hoping that this happy time might come."

The eloquence of Joe's arm surpassed the most

impassioned language; and so did that of his lips—yet he said nothing, either.

"And now, at last," cried Dolly, trembling with the fervour of her speech, "if you were sick, and shattered in your every limb; if you were ailing, weak, and sorrowful; if, instead of being what you are, you were in everybody's eyes but mine the wreck and ruin of a man, I would be your wife, dear love, with greater pride and joy, than if you were the stateliest lord in England!"

"What have I done," cried Joe—"What have I done to meet with this reward?"

"You have taught me," said Dolly, raising her pretty face to his, "to know myself, and your worth; to be something better than I was; to be more deserving of your true love and manly nature. In years to come, dear Joe, you shall find that you have done so; for I will be, not only now, when we are young and full of hope, but when we have grown old and weary, your patient, gentle, never-tiring wife. I will never know a wish or care beyond our home and you, and I will always study how to please you with my best affection and my most devoted love. I will—indeed I will!"

Joe could only repeat his former eloquence—but it was very much to the purpose.

BARNABY RUDGE

## SYDNEY CARTON'S AVOWAL

If Sydney Carton ever shone anywhere, he certainly never shone in the house of Doctor Manette. He had been there often, during a whole year, and had always been the same moody and morose lounger there,

When he cared to talk, he talked well; but the cloud of caring for nothing, which overshadowed him with such a fatal darkness, was very rarely pierced by the light within him. . . .

On a day in August . . . from being irresolute and purposeless, his feet became animated by an intention, and, in the working out of that intention, they took him to the doctor's door.

He was shown upstairs, and found Lucie at her work, alone. . . . She had never been quite at her ease with him, and received him with some little embarrassment as he seated himself near her table. But, looking up at his face in the interchange of the first few commonplaces, she observed a change in it.

"I fear you are not well, Mr. Carton!"

"No. But the life I lead, Miss Manette, is not conducive to health. What is to be expected of, or by, such profligates?"

"Is it not—forgive me; I have begun the question on my lips—a pity to live no better life?"

"God knows it is a shame!"

"Then why not change it?"

Looking gently at him again, she was surprised and saddened to see that there were tears in his eyes. There were tears in his voice, too, as he answered:

"It is too late for that. I shall never be better than I am. I shall sink lower, and be worse."

He leaned an elbow on her table, and covered his eyes with his hand. The table trembled in the silence that followed. . . .

'If it had been possible, Miss Manette, that you could have returned the love of the man you see before you—self-flung away, wasted, drunken, poor creature of misuse as you know him to be—he would have been conscious this day and hour, in spite of his happiness, that he would bring you to misery, bring you to sorrow and repentance, blight you, disgrace you, pull you down with him. I know very well that you can have no tenderness for me; I ask for none; I am even thankful that it cannot be.

"Without it, can I not save you, Mr. Carton? Can I not recall you—forgive me again!—to a better course? Can I in no way repay your confidence? I know this is a confidence," she modestly said, after a little hesitation, and in earnest tears, "I know you would say this to no one else. Can I turn it to no good account for yourself, Mr. Carton?"

He shook his head.

"To none. No, Miss Manette, to none. If you will hear me through a very little more, all you can ever do for me is done. . . .

"Be under no apprehension, Miss Manette, of my resuming this conversation by so much as a passing word. I will never refer to it again. If I were dead, that could not be surer than it is henceforth. In the hour of my death, I shall hold sacred the one good remembrance—and shall thank and bless you for it—that my last avowal of myself was made to you, and that my name, and faults, and miseries, were gently carried in your heart. May it otherwise be light and happy! . . .

"My last supplication of all, is this; and with it, I will relieve you of a visitor with whom I well know you have nothing in unison, and between whom and you there is an impassable space. It is useless to say it, I know, but it rises out of my soul. For you, and for any dear to you, I would do anything. If my career were of that better kind that there was any opportunity or capacity of sacrifice in it, I would embrace any sacrifice for you and for those dear to you. Try to hold me in your mind, at some quiet times, as ardent and sincere in this one thing. The time will come, the time will not be long in coming, when new ties will be formed about you—ties that will bind you yet more tenderly and strongly to the home you so adorn—the dearest ties that will ever grace and gladden you. O Miss Manette, when the little picture of a happy father's face looks up in yours, when you see your own bright beauty springing up anew at your feet, think now and then that there is a man who would give his life, to keep a life you love beside you!"

He said, "Farewell!" said a last "God bless you!" and left her.

A TALE OF TWO CITIES

## LET'S HAVE A WEDDING

When we had fortified ourselves with the rum-and-milk and biscuits, and were going out for the walk with that training preparation on us, I was considerably surprised to see Wemmick take up a fishing-rod, and put it over his shoulder. "Why, we are not going fishing!" said I. "No," returned Wemmick, "but I like to walk with one."

I thought this odd; however, I said nothing, and we set off. We went towards Camberwell Green, and when we were thereabouts, Wemmick said suddenly:

"Halloa! Here's a church!"

There was nothing very surprising in that; but again, I was rather surprised, when he said, as if he were animated by a brilliant idea:

"Let's go in!"

We went in, Wemmick, leaving his fishing-rod in the porch, and looked all round. In the meantime, Wemmick was diving into his coat-pockets, and getting something out of paper there.

"Halloa!" said he. "Here's a couple of pairs of gloves! Let's put 'em on!"

As the gloves were white kid gloves . . . I now began to have my strong suspicions. They were strengthened into certainty when I beheld the Aged enter at a side door, escorting a lady.

"Halloa!" said Wemmick. "Here's Miss Skiffins! Let's have a wedding."

That discreet damsel was attired as usual, except that she was now engaged in substituting for her green kid gloves, a pair of white. The Aged was likewise occupied in preparing a similar sacrifice for the altar of Hymen. The old gentleman, however, experienced so much difficulty in getting his gloves on, that Wemmick found it necessary to put him with his back against a pillar, and then get behind the pillar himself and pull away at them, while I for my part held the old gentleman round the waist, that he might present an equal and safe resistance. By dint of this ingenious scheme, his gloves were got on to perfection.

The clerk and clergyman then appearing, we were ranged in order at those fatal rails. True to his notion of seeming to do all without preparation, I heard Wemmick say to himself as he took something out of his waistcoat-pocket before the service began, "Halloa! Here's a ring!"

I acted in the capacity of backer, or best-man, to the bridegroom; while a little limp pew-opener, in a soft bonnet like a baby's, made a feint of being a bosom friend of Miss Skiffins. The responsibility of giving the lady away devolved upon the Aged, which led to the clergyman's being unintentionally scandalised, and it happened thus. When he said, "Who giveth this woman to be married to this man?" the old gentleman, not in the least knowing what point of the ceremony we had arrived at, stood most amiably beaming at the Ten Commandments. Upon which, the clergyman said again, "Who giveth this woman to be married to this man?" The old gentleman being still in a state of most estimable unconsciousness, the bridegroom cried out in his accustomed voice, "Now, aged P., you know; who giveth?" To which the Aged replied with great briskness, before saying that *he* gave, "All right, John, all right, my boy!" And the clergyman came to so gloomy a pause upon it, that I had doubts for the moment whether we should get completely married that day.

It was completely done, however, and when we were going out of church, Wemmick took the cover off the font, and put his white gloves in it, and put the cover on again. Mrs. Wemmick, more heedful of the future, put her white gloves in her pocket and assumed her green. "*Now*, Mr. Pip," said Wemmick, triumphantly shouldering the fishing-rod as we came out, "let me ask you whether anybody would suppose this to be a wedding-party!"

GREAT EXPECTATIONS

## MR. BARKIS'S WOOING

... Mr. Barkis appeared in an exceedingly vacant and awkward condition, and with a bundle of oranges tied up in a handkerchief. As he made no allusion of any kind to this property, he was supposed to have left it behind him by accident when he went away; until Ham, running after him to restore it, came back with the information that it was intended for Peggotty. After that occasion he appeared every evening at exactly the same hour, and always with a little bundle, to which he never alluded, and which he regularly put behind the door, and left there. These offerings of affection were of a most various and eccentric description. Among them I remember a double set of pigs' trotters, a huge pin-cushion, half a bushel or so of apples, a pair of jet earrings, some Spanish onions, a box of dominoes, a canary bird and cage, and a leg of pickled pork.

Mr. Barkis's wooing, as I remember it, was altogether of a peculiar kind. He very seldom said anything; but he would sit by the fire in much the same attitude as he sat in his cart, and stare heavily at Peggotty, who was opposite. One night, being, as I suppose, inspired by love, he made a dart at the bit of wax-candle she kept for her thread, and put it in his waistcoat-pocket and carried it off. After that, his great delight was to produce it when it was wanted, sticking to the lining of his pocket, in a partially melted state, and pocket it again when it was done with. He seemed to enjoy himself very much, and not to feel at all called upon to talk. Even when he took Peggotty out for a walk on the flats, he had no uneasiness on that head, I believe; contenting himself with now and then asking her if she was pretty comfortable; and I remember that sometimes, after he was gone, Peggotty would throw her apron over her face, and laugh for half-an-hour. Indeed, we were all more or less amused, except that miserable Mrs Gummidge, whose courtship would appear to have been of an exactly parallel nature, she was so continually reminded by these transactions of the old one.

DAVID COPPERFIELD

## A PROPOSAL—WITHOUT PREJUDICE

". . . My present salary, Miss Mummerson, at Kenge and Carboy's, is two pound a week. When I first had the happiness of looking upon you, it was one-fifteen, and had stood at that figure for a lengthened period. A rise of five has since taken place, and a further rise of five is guaranteed at the expiration of a term not exceeding twelve months from the present date. My mother has a little property, which takes the form of a small life annuity; upon which she lives in an independent though unassuming manner, in the Old Street Road. She is eminently calculated for a mother-in-law. She never interferes, is all for peace, and her disposition easy. She has her failings—as who has not?—but I never knew her to do it when company was present; at which time you may freely trust her with wines, spirits, or malt liquors. My own abode is lodgings in Penton Place, Pentonville. It is lowly, but airy, open at the back, and considered one of the 'ealthiest outlets. Miss Summerson! in the mildest language, I adore you. Would you be so kind as to allow me (as I may say) to file a declaration—to make an offer!"

Mr. Guppy went down on his knees. . . .

"I should be pained, Mr. Guppy," said I, rising and puting my hand on the bell-rope, "to do you, or anyone who was sincere, the injustice of slighting any honest feeling, however disagreeably expressed. If you have really meant to give me a proof of your good opinion, though ill-timed and misplaced, I feel that I ought to thank you. I have very little reason to be proud, and I am not proud. I hope," I think I added, without very well knowing what I said, "that you will now go away as if you had never been so exceedingly foolish, and attend to Messrs. Kenge and Carboy's business."

"Half a minute, miss!" cried Mr. Guppy, checking me as I was about to ring. "This has been without prejudice?"

"I will never mention it," said I, "unless you give me future occasion to do so."

"A quarter of a minute, miss! In case you should think better—at any time, however distant, *that's* no consequence, for my feelings can never alter—of anything I have said. . . . Mr. William Guppy, eighty-seven, Penton Place, or if removed, or dead (of blighted hopes or anything of that sort), care of Mrs. Guppy, three hundred and two, Old Street Road, will be sufficient."

BLEAK HOUSE

## A LOVER COMPOSES SOME EPITAPHS

Young John was small of stature, with rather weak legs and very weak light hair. . . . Young John was gentle likewise. But he was great of soul. Poetical, expansive, faithful.

Though too humble before the ruler of his heart to be sanguine, young John had considered the object of his attachment in all its lights and shades. Following it out to blissful results, he had descried, without self-commendation, a fitness in it. Say things prospered, and they were united. She was the child of the Marshalsea; he, the lock-keeper. There was a fitness in that. Say he became a resident turnkey. She would officially succeed to the chamber she had rented so long. There was a beautiful propriety in that. It looked over the wall if you stood on tip-toe; and, with the trellis-work of scarlet beans and a canary or so, would become a very Arbour. . . . They would glide down the stream of time, in pastoral domestic happiness. Young John drew tears from his eyes by finishing the picture with a tombstone in the adjoining churchyard, close against the prison wall, bearing the following touching inscription: "Sacred to the memory of JOHN CHIVERY, Sixty years Turnkey, and fifty years Head Turnkey, of the neighbouring Marshalsea, Who departed this life, universally respected, on the thirty-first of December, One thousand eight hundred and eighty-six, Aged eighty-three years. Also of his truly beloved and truly loving wife, AMY, whose maiden name was Dorrit, who survived his loss not quite forty-eight hours, And who breathed her last in the Marshalsea aforesaid. There she was born, There she lived, There she died."

### *Alas, young John's suit found no favour and he composed a new epitaph*

It was an affecting illustration of the fallacy of human projects to behold her lover . . . creeping along by the worst back streets, and composing as he went, the following new inscription for a tombstone in St. George's Churchyard:

"Here lie the mortal remains of JOHN CHIVERY, Never anything worth mentioning. Who died about the end of the year one thousand eight hundred and twenty-six, Of a broken heart, Requesting with his last breath that the word AMY might be inscribed over his ashes, Which was accordingly directed to be done, By his afflicted Parents."

### *Delivering a letter to the Father of the Marshalsea, and finding Little Dorrit in tears*

. . . Mr. Chivery, junior, went his way, having spontaneously composed on the spot an entirely new epitaph for himself, to the effect that Here lay the body of John Chivery, Who, Having at such a date, Beheld the idol of his life, In grief and tears, And feeling unable to bear the harrowing spectacle, Immediately repaired to the abode of his inconsolable parents, And terminated his existence by his own rash act.

*And when at last John Chivery found Arthur Clennam a prisoner in the Marshalsea*

. . . Young John lay wrapped in peaceful slumber, after composing and arranging the following monumental inscription on his pillow:—

STRANGER!
RESPECT THE TOMB OF
JOHN CHIVERY, JUNIOR,
WHO DIED AT AN ADVANCED AGE
NOT NECESSARY TO MENTION.
HE ENCOUNTERED HIS RIVAL IN A
DISTRESSED STATE,
AND FELT INCLINED
TO HAVE A ROUND WITH HIM;
BUT, FOR THE SAKE OF THE LOVED ONE,
CONQUERED THOSE FEELINGS OF
BITTERNESS, AND BECAME
MAGNANIMOUS

LITTLE DORRIT

# 3

# *Husbands and Wives*

MERCY CHUZZLEWIT'S WELCOME HOME

As the door closed heavily behind them, Mrs. Jonas sat down in a chair and felt a strange chill creep upon her, whilst she looked about the room. It was pretty much as she had known it, but appeared more dreary. She had thought to see it brightened to receive her.

"It ain't good enough for you, I suppose?" said Jonas, watching her looks.

"Why, it *is* dull," said Mercy, trying to be more herself.

"It'll be duller before you're done with it," retorted Jonas, "if you give me any of your airs. You're a nice article to turn sulky on first coming home! Ecod, you used to have life enough, when you could plague me with it. The gal's downstairs. Ring the bell for supper, while I take my boots off!"

She roused herself from looking after him as he left the room, to do what he desired: when the old man Chuffey laid his hand softly on her arm.

"You are not married?" he said eagerly. "Not married?"

"Yes. A month ago. Good Heaven, what is the matter?"

He answered nothing was the matter; and turned from her. But in her fear and wonder, turning also, she saw him raise his trembling hands above his head, and heard him say:

"Oh! woe, woe, woe, upon this wicked house!"

It was her welcome—HOME.

MARTIN CHUZZLEWIT

## MY CHILD-WIFE LOVES ME

"Will you call me a name I want you to call me?" inquired Dora.

"What is it?" I asked with a smile.

"It's a stupid name," she said, shaking her curls for a moment. "Child-wife."

I laughingly asked my child-wife what her fancy was in desiring to be so called. She answered without moving, otherwise than as the arm I twined about her may have brought her blue eyes nearer to me:

"I don't mean, you silly fellow, that you should use

the name instead of Dora. I only mean that you should think of me that way. When you are going to be angry with me, say to yourself, 'it's only my child-wife!' When I am very disappointing, say, 'I knew, a long time ago, that she would make but a child-wife!' When you miss what I should like to be, and I think can never be, say, 'still my foolish child-wife loves me!' For indeed I do."

DAVID COPPERFIELD

## A VENERABLE SUPERANNUATED COUPLE

At the present time, in the dark little parlour certain feet below the level of the street—a grim, hard, uncouth parlour, only ornamented with the coarsest of baize table-covers, and the hardest of sheet-iron tea-trays, and offering in its decorative character no bad allegorical representation of Grandfather Smallweed's mind—seated in two black horse-hair porter's chairs, one on each side of the fire-place, the superannuated Mr. and Mrs. Smallweed wile away the rosy hours. On the stove are a couple of trivets for the pots and kettles which it is Grandfather Smallweed's usual occupation to watch, and projecting from the chimney-piece between them is a sort of brass gallows for roasting, which he also superintends when it is in action. Under the venerable Mr. Smallweed's seat, and guarded by his spindle legs, is a drawer in his chair, reported to contain property to a fabulous amount. Beside him is a spare cushion, with which he is always provided, in order that he may have something to throw at the venerable partner of his respected age whenever she makes an allusion to money—a subject on which he is particularly sensitive.

BLEAK HOUSE

## MRS. POTT MAKES A MILD PROTEST

Mrs. Pott received Mr. Pickwick's paternal grasp of the hand with enchanting sweetness; and Mr. Winkle, who had not been announced at all, sidled and bowed, unnoticed, in an obscure corner.

"P. my dear——" said Mrs. Pott.

"My life," said Mr. Pott.

"Pray introduce the other gentleman."

"I beg a thousand pardons," said Mr. Pott. "Permit me, Mrs. Pott, Mr.——"

"Winkle," said Mr. Pickwick.

"Winkle," echoed Mr. Pott; and the ceremony of introduction was complete.

"We owe you many apologies, ma'am," said Mr. Pickwick, "for disturbing your domestic arrangements at so short a notice."

"I beg you won't mention it, sir," replied the feminine Pott, with vivacity. "It is a high treat to me, I assure you, to see any new faces; living as I do, from day to day, and week to week, in this dull place, and seeing nobody."

"Nobody, my dear!" exclaimed Mr. Pott, archly.

"Nobody but *you*," retorted Mrs. Pott, with asperity.

"You see, Mr. Pickwick," said the host in explanation of his wife's lament, "that we are in some measure cut off from many enjoyments and pleasures of which we might otherwise partake. My public station, as editor of the *Eatanswill Gazette*, the position which the paper holds in the country, my constant immersion in the vortex of politics——"

"P. my dear——" interposed Mrs. Pott.

"My life——" said the editor.

"I wish, my dear, you would endeavour to find some topic of conversation in which these gentlemen might take some rational interest."

"But, my love," said Mr. Pott, with great humility, "Mr. Pickwick does take an interest in it."

"It's well for him if he can," said Mrs. Pott emphatically; "I am wearied out of my life with your politics, and quarrels with the *Independent*, and nonsense. I am quite astonished, P., at your making such as exhibtion of your absurdity."

"But, my dear——" said Mr. Pott.

"Oh, nonsense, don't talk to me," said Mrs. Pott. 'Do you play écarté, sir?"

"I shall be happy to learn under your tuition," replied Mr. Winkle.

PICKWICK PAPERS

## THE AGGRAVATING MR. NUPKINS

Mrs. Nupkins was a majestic female in a pink gauze turban and a light-brown wig. Miss Nupkins possessed all her mama's haughtiness without the turban, and all her ill-nature without the wig; and whenever the exercise of these two amiable qualities involved mother and daughter in some unpleasant dilemma, as they not infrequently did, they both concurred in laying the blame on the shoulders of Mr. Nupkins. Accordingly, when Mr. Nupkins sought Mrs. Nupkins, and detailed the communication which had been made by Mr. Pickwick, Mrs. Nupkins suddenly recollected that she had always expected something of the kind; that she had always said it would come to be so; that her advice was never taken; that she really did not know what Mr. Nupkins supposed she was; and so forth.

"The idea!" said Miss Nupkins, forcing a tear of very scanty proportions into the corner of each eye, "the idea of my being made such a fool of!"

"Ah! you may thank your papa, my dear," said Mrs. Nupkins; "how I have implored and begged that man to inquire into the captain's family connections; how I have urged and entreated him to take some decisive step! I am quite certain that nobody would believe it—quite."

"But, my dear," said Mr. Nupkins.

"Don't talk to me, you aggravating thing, don't!" said Mrs. Nupkins.

PICKWICK PAPERS

## MR. WELLER'S SECOND WENTUR

"Wy, I'll tell you what, Sammy," said Mr. Weller, senior, with much solemnity in his manner, "there never was a nicer woman as a widder than that 'ere second wentur of mine—a sweet creetur she was, Sammy; all I can say on her now, is, that as she was such an uncommon pleasant widder, it's a great pity that she ever changed her con-dition. She don't act as a vife, Sammy."

"Don't she, though?" inquired Mr. Weller, junior.

The elder Mr. Weller shook his head, as he replied

with a sigh, "I've done it once too often, Sammy; I've done it once too often. Take example by your father, my boy, and be wery careful o' widders all your life, especially if they've kept a public-house, Sammy."

* * *

". . . How's mother-in-law this mornin'?"

"Queer, Sammy, queer," replied the elder Mr. Weller, with impressive gravity. "She's been gettin' rayther in the methodistical order, lately, Sammy; and she is uncommon pious, to be sure. She's too good a creetur for me, Sammy. I feel I don't deserve her."

"Ah," said Mr. Samuel, "that's wery self-denyin' o' you."

"Wery," replied his parent, with a sigh. "She's got hold o' some inwention for grown-up people being born again, Sammy; the new birth, I think they calls it. I should wery much like to see that system in haction, Sammy. I should wery much like to see your mother-in-law born again. Wouldn't I put her out to nurse!"

PICKWICK PAPERS

## THE LOYALTY OF MRS. MICAWBER

"He is the parent of my children! He is the father of my twins! He is the husband of my affections and I ne-ver-will-desert Mr. Micawber."

DAVID COPPERFIELD

## THREE DISTINGUISHED HUSBANDS

Mr. Bayham Badger was a pink, fresh-faced, crisp-looking gentleman, with a weak voice, white teeth, light hair, and surprised eyes; some years younger, I should say, than Mrs. Bayham Badger. He admired her exceedingly, but principally, and to begin with, on the curious ground (as it seemed to us) of her having had three husbands. We had barely taken our seats, when he said to Mr. Jarndyce quite triumphantly,

"You would hardly suppose that I am Mrs. Bayham Badger's third!"

"Indeed?" said Mr. Jarndyce.

"Her third!" said Mr. Badger. "Mrs. Bayham Badger has not the appearance, Miss Summerson, of a lady who has had two former husbands?"

I said, "Not at all!"

"And most remarkable men!" said Mr. Badger. In a tone of confidence. "Captain Swosser of the Royal Navy, who was Mrs. Badger's first husband, was a very distinguished officer indeed. The name of Professor Dingo, my immediate predecessor, is one of European reputation."

Mrs. Badger overheard him, and smiled.

"Yes, my dear!" Mr. Badger replied to the smile, "I was observing to Mr. Jarndyce and Miss Summerson, that you had had two former husabnds—both very distinguished men. And they found it, as people generally do, difficult to believe."

"I was barely twenty," said Mrs. Badger, "when I married Captain Swosser of the Royal Navy. I was in the Mediterranean with him; I am quite a Sailor.

On the twelfth anniversary of my wedding-day, I became the wife of Professor Dingo."

("Of European reputation," added Mr. Badger in an undertone.)

"And when Mr. Badger and myself were married," pursued Mrs. Badger, "we were married on the same day of the year. I had become attached to the day."

"So that Mrs. Badger has been married to three husbands—two of them highly distinguished men," said Mr. Badger summing up the facts; "and, each time, upon the twenty-first of March at Eleven in the forenoon!"

We all expressed our admiration.

"But for Mr. Badger's modesty," said Mr. Jarndyce, "I would take leave to correct him, and say three distinguished men."

"Thank you, Mr. Jarndyce! What I always tell him!" observed Mrs. Badger.

"And, my dear," said Mr. Badger, "what do *I* always tell you? That without any affectation of disparaging such professional distinction as I may have attained (which our friend Mr. Carstone will have many opportunities of estimating), I am not so weak —no, really," said Mr. Badger to us generally, "so unreasonable—as to put my reputation on the same footing with such first-rate men as Captain Swosser and Professor Dingo. Perhaps you may be interested, Mr. Jarndyce," continued Mr. Bayham Badger, leading the way into the next drawing-room, "in this portrait of Captain Swosser. It was taken on his return home from the African Station, where he had suffered from the fever of the country. Mrs. Badger considers it too yellow. But it's a very fine head. A very fine head!"

We all echoed, "A very fine head!"

"I feel when I look at it," said Mr. Badger, " 'that's a man I should like to have seen!' It strikingly bespeaks the first-class man that Captain Swosser pre-eminently was. On the other side, Professor Dingo. I knew him well—attended him in his last illness—a speaking likeness! Over the piano, Mrs. Bayham Badger when Mrs. Swosser. Over the sofa, Mrs. Bayham Badger when Mrs. Dingo. Of Mrs. Bayham Badger *in esse*, I possess the original, and have no copy."

BLEAK HOUSE

## MR. BUMBLE'S LAMENTATION

Mr. Bumble had married Mrs. Corney, and was master of the workhouse. Another beadle had come into power. On him the cocked hat, gold-laced coat, and staff, had all three descended.

"And to-morrow two months it was done!" said Mr. Bumble with a sigh. "It seems a age."

Mr. Bumble might have meant that he had concentrated a whole existence of happiness into the short space of eight weeks; but the sigh—there was a vast deal of meaning in the sigh.

"I sold myself," said Mr. Bumble, pursuing the same train of reflection, "for six teaspoons, a pair of sugar-tongs, and a milk-pot; with a small quantity of second-hand furniture, and twenty pound in money. I went very reasonable. Cheap, dirt cheap!"

"Cheap!" cried a shrill voice in Mr. Bumble's ear:

"you would have been dear at any price; and dear enough I paid for you, Lord above knows that!"

Mr. Bumble turned and encountered the face of his interesting consort, who, imperfectly comprehending the few words she had overheard of his complaint, had hazarded the forgoing remark at a venture.

"Mrs. Bumble, ma'am!" said Mr. Bumble with sentimental sternness.

"Well!" cried the lady.

"Have the goodness to look at me," said Mr. Bumble, fixing his eyes upon her. ("If she stands such a eye as that," said Mr. Bumble to himself, "she can stand anything. It is a eye I never knew to fail with paupers. If it fails with her, my power is gone.")

Whether an exceedingly small expansion of eye be sufficient to quell paupers, who, being lightly fed, are in no very high condition; or whether the late Mrs. Corney was particularly proof against eagle glances; are matters of opinion. The matter of fact is, that the matron was in no way overpowered by Mr. Bumble's scowl, but, on the contrary, treated it with great disdain, and even raised a laugh thereat, which sounded as though it were genuine.

On hearing this most unexpected sound, Mr. Bumble looked, first incredulous, and afterwards amazed. He then relapsed into his former state; nor did he rouse himself until his attention was again awakened by the voice of his partner.

"Are you going to sit snoring there, all day?" inquired Mrs. Bumble.

"I am going to sit here, as long as I think proper, ma'am," rejoined Mr. Bumble; "and although I was not snoring, I shall snore, gape, sneeze, laugh, or cry, as the humour strikes me; such being my prerogative."

"Your prerogative!" sneered Mrs. Bumble, with ineffable contempt.

"I said the word, ma'am," said Mr. Bumble. "The prerogative of a man is to command."

"And what is the prerogative of a woman, in the name of Goodness?" cried the relict of Mr. Corney deceased.

"To obey, ma'am," thundered Mr. Bumble. "Your late unfortunate husband should have taught it you; and then, perhaps, he might have been alive now. I wish he was, poor man!"

OLIVER TWIST

## DISCIPLINE MUST BE MAINTAINED

"George, you know the old girl—she's as sweet and as mild as milk. But touch her on the children—or myself—and she's off like gunpowder."

"It does her credit, Mat!"

"George," said Mr. Bagnet, looking straight before him, "the old girl—can't do anything—that don't do her credit. More or less. I never say so. Discipline must be maintained."

"She's worth her weight in gold," said the trooper.

"In gold?" says Mrs. Bagnet. "I'll tell you what. The old girl's weight—is twelve stone six. Would I take that weight—in any metal—*for* the old girl? No. Why not? Because the old girl's metal is far more precious—than the preciousest metal. And she's *all* metal!"

"You are right, Mat!"

"When she took me and accepted of the ring—she

'listed under me and the children—heart and head; for life. She's that earnest," says Mr. Bagnet, "and true to her colours—that, touch us with a finger—and she turns out—and stands to her arms. If the old girl fires wide—once in a way—at the call of duty—look over it, George. For she's loyal!"

BLEAK HOUSE

## MRS. CRUNCHER AT IT AGIN!

Mr. Cruncher reposed under a patchwork counterpane, like a Harlequin at home. At first, he slept heavily, but, by degrees, began to roll and surge in bed, until he rose above the surface with his spiky hair looking as if it must tear the sheets to ribbons. At which juncture, he exclaimed, in a voice of dire exasperation: "Bust me, if she ain't at it agin!"

A woman of orderly and industrious appearance rose from her knees in a corner, with sufficient haste and trepidation to show that she was the person referred to.

"What!" said Mr. Cruncher, looking out of bed for a boot. "You're at it agin, are you?"

After hailing the morn with this second salutation, he threw a boot at the woman as a third. . . .

"What," said Mr. Cruncher, varying his apostrophe after missing his mark—"What are you up to, Aggerawayter?"

"I was only saying my prayers."

"Saying your prayers! You're a nice woman! What do you mean by flopping yourself down and praying agin me?"

"I was not praying against you; I was praying for you."

"You weren't. And if you were, I won't be took the liberty with. Here! your mother's a nice woman, young Jerry, going a-praying agin your father's prosperity. You've got a dutiful mother, you have, my son. You've got a religious mother, you have, my boy: going and flopping herself down, and praying that the bread-and-butter may be snatched out of the mouth of her only child."

A TALE OF TWO CITIES

## A PREY TO PROSPERITY

". . . and it's pleasant to know that you are Mrs. Boffin," said her husband, "and it's been a pleasant thing to know this many and many a year."

These two ignorant and unpolished people had guided themselves so far on in their journey of life, by a religious sense of duty and desire to do right. Ten thousand weaknesses and absurdities might have been detected in the breasts of both; ten thousand vanities additional, possibly, in the breast of the woman. But, the hard, wrathful, and sordid nature that had wrung as much work out of them as could be got in their best days, for as little money as could be paid to hurry on their worst, had never been so warped but that it knew their moral straightness and respected it. In its own despite, in a constant conflict with itself and them, it had done so. And this is the eternal law. For, Evil often stops short at itself and dies with the doer of it! but Good, never.

*   *   *

Mr. and Mrs. Boffin sat after breakfast, in the Bower, a prey to prosperity.

OUR MUTUAL FRIEND

## MRS. VARDEN ALL CONTRARY

Mrs. Varden was a lady of what is commonly called an uncertain temper—a phrase which being interpreted signifies a temper tolerably certain to make everybody more or less uncomfortable. Thus it generally happened, that when other people were merry, Mrs. Varden was dull; and that when other people were dull, Mrs. Varden was disposed to be amazingly cheerful. Indeed the worthy housewife was of such a capricious nature, that she not only attained a higher pitch of genius than Macbeth, in respect of her ability to be wise, amazed, temperate and furious, loyal and neutral in an instant, but would sometimes ring the changes backwards and forwards on all possible moods and flights in one short quarter of an hour; performing, as it were, a kind of triple bob major on the peal of instruments in the female belfry, with a skilfulness and rapidity of execution that astonished all who heard her.

* * *

"How do you find yourself now, my dear?" said the locksmith, taking a chair near his wife (who had resumed her book), and rubbing his knees hard as he made the inquiry.

"You're very anxious to know, an't you?" returned Mrs. Varden, with her eyes upon the print. "You, that have not been near me all day, and wouldn't have been if I was dying!"

"My dear Martha——" said Gabriel.

Mrs. Varden turned over the next page; then went back again to the bottom line overleaf to be quite sure of the last words; and then went on reading with an appearance of the deepest interest and study.

"My dear Martha," said the locksmith, "how can you say such things, when you know you don't mean them? If you were dying! Why, if there was anything serious the matter with you, Martha, shouldn't I be in constant attendance upon you?"

"Yes!" cried Mrs. Varden, bursting into tears, "yes, you would. I don't doubt it, Varden. Certainly you would. That's as much as to tell me that you would be hovering round me like a vulture, waiting till the breath was out of my body, that you might go and marry somebody else."

BARNABY RUDGE

# 4

# *Law and Lawyers*

## BROWBEATING AS A FINE ART

A highly popular murder had been committed, and Mr. Wopsle was imbrued in blood to the eyebrows. He gloated over every abhorrent adjective in the description, and identified himself with every witness at the inquest. He faintly moaned, "I am done for," as the victim; and he barbarously bellowed, "I'll serve you out," as the murderer. He gave the medical testimony, in pointed imitation of our local practitioner; and he piped and shook, as the aged turnpike-keeper who had heard blows, to an extent so very paralytic as to suggest a doubt regarding the mental competency of that witness. The coroner, in Mr. Wopsle's hands, became Timon of Athens; the beadle, Coriolanus. He enjoyed himself thoroughly, and we all enjoyed ourselves, and were delightfully comfortable. In this cosy state of mind we came to the verdict, Wilful Murder.

Then, and not sooner, I became aware of a strange gentleman leaning over the back of the settle opposite me, looking on. There was an expression of contempt on his face, and he bit the side of a great forefinger as he watched the group of faces. "Well!" said the stranger to Mr. Wopsle, when the reading was done, "you have settled it all to your own satisfaction, I have no doubt?"

Everybody started and looked up, as if it were the murderer. He looked at everybody coldly and sarcastically.

"Guilty, of course?" said he. "Out with it. Come!"

"Sir," returned Mr. Wopsle, "without having the honour of your acquaintance, I do say Guilty." Upon this we all took courage to unite in a confirmatory murmur.

"I know you do," said the stranger; "I knew you would. I told you so. But now I'll ask you a question. Do you know, or do you not know, that the law of England supposes every man to be innocent until he is proved—proved—to be guilty?"

"Sir," Mr. Wopsle began to reply, "as an Englishman myself, I——"

"Come!" said the stranger, biting his forefinger at him. "Don't evade the question. Either you know it, or you don't know it. Which is it to be?"

He stood with his head on one side and himself on one side, in a bullying interrogative manner, and he threw his forefinger at Mr. Wopsle—as it were to mark him out—before biting it again.

"Now!" said he. "Do you know it, or don't you know it?"

"Certainly I know it," replied Mr. Wopsle.

"Certainly you know it. Then why didn't you say so at first? Now, I'll ask you another question;" taking possession of Mr. Wopsle as if he had a right to him. "*Do* you know that none of these witnesses have yet been cross-examined?"

Mr. Wopsle was beginning, "I can only say——" when the stranger stopped him.

"What? You won't answer the question, yes or no? Now, I'll try again." Throwing his finger at him again, "Attend to me. Are you aware, or are you not aware, that none of these witnesses have yet been cross-examined? Come, I only want one word from you. Yes, or no?"

Mr. Wopsle hesitated, and we all began to conceive rather a poor opinion of him.

"Come!" said the stranger. "I'll help you. You don't deserve help, but I'll help you. Look at that paper you hold in your hand. What is it?"

"What is it?" repeated Mr. Wopsle, eyeing it, much at a loss.

"Is it," pursued the stranger in his most sarcastic and supicious manner, "the printed paper you have just been reading from?"

"Undoubtedly."

"Undoubtedly. Now, turn to that paper, and tell me whether it distinctly states that the prisoner expressly said that his legal advisers instructed him altogether to reserve his defence?"

"I read that just now," Mr. Wopsle pleaded.

"Never mind what you read just now, sir; I don't ask you what you read just now. You may read the Lord's Prayer backwards, if you like—and, perhaps, have done it before to-day. Turn to the paper. No, no, no, my friend; not to the top of the column; you know better than that; to the bottom, to the bottom." (We all began to think Mr. Wopsle full of subterfuge.) "Well? have you found it?"

"Here it is," said Mr. Wopsle.

"Now, follow that passage with your eye, and tell me whether it distinctly states that the prisoner expressly said that he was instructed by his legal advisers wholly to reserve his defence? Come! Do you make that of it?"

Mr. Wopsle answered, "Those are not the exact words."

"Not the exact words!" repeated the gentleman bitterly. "Is that the exact substance?"

"Yes," said Mr. Wopsle.

"Yes," repeated the stranger, looking round at the rest of the company with his right hand extended towards the witness, Wopsle. "And now I ask you what you say to the conscience of that man who, with that passage before his eyes, can lay his head upon his pillow after having pronounced a fellow-creature guilty, unheard?"

We all began to suspect that Mr. Wopsle was not the man we had thought him, and that he was beginning to be found out.

"And that same man, remember," pursued the

gentleman, throwing his finger at Mr. Wopsle heavily; "that same man might be summoned as a juryman upon this very trial, and, having thus deeply committed himself, might return to the bosom of his family, and lay his head upon his pillow after deliberately swearing that he would well and truly try the issue between our Sovereign Lord the King and the prisoner at the bar, and would a true verdict give according to the evidence, so help him God!"

We were all deeply persuaded that the unfortunate Wopsle had gone too far, and had better stop in his reckless career while there was yet time.

GREAT EXPECTATIONS

## BIRDS IN CHANCERY

"Extremely honoured, I am sure," said our poor hostess, with the greatest suavity, "by this visit from the wards in Jarndyce. And very much indebted for the omen. It is a retired situation. Considering. I am limited as to situation. In consequence of the necessity of attending on the Chancellor. I have lived here many years. I pass my days in court; my evenings and my nights here. I find the nights long, for I sleep but little, and think much. That is, of course, unavoidable; being in Chancery. I am sorry I cannot offer chocolate. I expect a judgment shortly, and shall then place my establishment on a superior footing. At present, I don't mind confessing to the wards in Jarndyce (in strict confidence), that I sometimes find it difficult to keep up a genteel appearance. I have felt the cold here. I have felt something sharper than cold. It matters very little. Pray excuse the introduction of such mean topics."

She partly drew aside the curtain of the long low garret-window, and called our attention to a number of bird-cages hanging there: some, containing several birds. There were larks, linnets, and goldfinches—I should think at least twenty.

"I began to keep the little creatures," she said, "with an object the wards will readily comprehend. With the intention of restoring them to liberty. When my judgment should be given. Ye-es! They die in prison, though. Their lives, poor silly things, are so short in comparison with Chancery proceedings, that, one by one, the whole collection has died over and over again. I doubt, do you know, whether one of these, though they are all young, will live to be free! Ve-ry mortifying, is it not?"

* * *

"Another secret, my dear, I have added to my collection of birds."

"Really, Miss Flite?" said I, knowing how it pleased her to have her confidence received with an appearance of interest.

She nodded several times, and her face became overcast and gloomy. "Two more. I call them Wards in Jarndyce. They are caged up with all the others. With Hope, Joy, Youth, Peace, Rest, Life, Dust, Ashes, Waste, Want, Ruin, Despair, Madness, Death, Cunning, Folly, Words, Wigs, Rags, Sheepskin, Plunder, Precedent, Jargon, Gammon, and Spinach!"

The poor soul kissed me, with the most troubled look I had ever seen in her; and went her way. Her manner of running over the names of her birds, as if she were afraid of hearing them even from her own lips, quite chilled me.

BLEAK HOUSE

## THE SMOKE OF LITIGATION

Snitchley and Craggs had a snug little office on the old Battle Ground, where they drove a snug business, and fought a great many small pitched battles for a great many contending parties. Though it could hardly be said of these conflicts that they were running fights—for in truth they generally proceeded at a snail's pace—the part the Firm had in them came so far within the general denomination, that they now took a shot at this Plaintiff, and now aimed a chop at that Defendant, now made a heavy charge at an estate in Chancery; and now had some light skirmishing among an irregular body of small debtors, just as the occasion served, and the enemy happened to present himself. The Gazette was an important and profitable feature in some of their fields, as in the fields of greater renown; and in most of the Actions wherein they showed their generalship, it was afterwards observed by the combatants that they had great difficulty in making each other out, or in knowing with any degree of distinctness what they were about, in consequence of the vast amount of smoke by which they were surrounded.

The offices of Messrs. Snitchley and Craggs stood convenient, with an open door down two smooth steps, in the market-place; so that any angry farmer inclining towards hot water, might tumble into it at once. Their special council-chamber and hall of conference was an old back-room upstairs, with a low dark ceiling, which seemed to be knitting its brows gloomily in the consideration of tangled points of law. It was furnished with some high-backed leathern chairs, garnished with great goggle-eyed brass nails, of which, every here and there, two or three had fallen out—or had been picked out, perhaps, by the wandering thumbs and fore-fingers of bewildered clients. There was a framed print of a great judge in it, every curl of whose dreadful wig had made a man's hair stand on end. Bales of paper filled the dusty closets, shelves, and tables; and round the wainscot there were tiers of boxes, padlocked and fireproof, with people's names painted outside, which anxious visitors felt themselves, by a cruel enchantment, obliged to spell backwards and forwards, and to make anagrams of, while they sat, seeming to listen to Snitchley and Craggs, without comprehending one word of what they said.

CHRISTMAS BOOKS (THE BATTLE OF LIFE)

## A LEGAL AMAZON

Miss Sally Brass was a lady of thirty-five or thereabouts, of gaunt and bony figure and a resolute bearing, which, if it repressed the softer emotions of love and kept admirers at a distance, certainly inspired a feeling akin to awe in the breasts of those male strangers who had the happiness to approach her. In face she bore a striking resemblance to her brother, Sampson, so exact indeed, was the likeness between them, that had it consorted with Miss Brass's maiden modesty and gentle womanhood to have assumed her brother's clothes in a frolic and sat down beside him, it would have been difficult for the oldest friend of the family to determine which was Sampson and which Sally, especially as the lady carried upon her upper lip certain reddish demonstrations, which, if the imagination had been assisted by her attire, might have been mistaken for a beard. These were, however, in all probability, nothing more than eyelashes in a wrong place, as the eyes of Miss Brass were quite free from any such natural impertinences. In complexion Miss Brass was sallow—rather a dirty salllow, so to speak—but this hue was agreeably relieved by the healthy glow which mantled in the extreme tip of her laughing nose. Her voice was exceedingly impressive —deep and rich in quality, and, once heard, not easily forgotten. Her usual dress was a green gown, in colour not unlike the curtain of the office window, made tight to the figure, and terminating at the throat, where it was fastened behind by a peculiarly large and massive button. Feeling, no doubt, that simplicity and plainness are the soul of elegance, Miss Brass wore no collar or kerchief except upon her head, which was invariably ornamented with a brown gauze scarf, like the wing of the fabled vampire, and which, twined into any form that happened to suggest itself, formed an easy and graceful head-dress.

Such was Miss Brass in person. In mind she was of a strong and vigorous turn, having from her earliest youth devoted herself with uncommon ardour to the study of the law; not wasting her speculations upon its eagle flights, which are rare, but tracing it attentively through all the slippery and eel-like crawlings in which it commonly pursues its way. Nor had she, like so many persons of great intellect, confined herself to theory, or stopped short where practical usefulness begins; inasmuch as she could engross, fair-copy, fill up printed forms with perfect accuracy, and, in short, transact any ordinary duty of the office, down to pouncing a skin of parchment or mending a pen. It is difficult to understand how, possessed of these combined attractions, she should remain Miss Brass; but whether she had steeled her heart against mankind, or whether those who might have wooed and won her were deterred by fears that, being learned in the law, she might have too near her fingers' ends those particular statutes which regulate what are familiarly termed actions for breach, certain it is that she was still in a state of celibacy, and still in daily occupation of her old stool opposite to that of her brother, Sampson. And equally certain it is, by the way, that between these two stools a great many people had come to the ground.

THE OLD CURIOSITY SHOP

## THE ORDEAL OF MR. WINKLE

"Now, sir," said Mr. Skimpin, "have the goodness to let his Lordship and the jury know what your name is, will you?" and Mr. Skimpin inclined his head on one side to listen with great sharpness to the answer, and glanced at the jury meanwhile, as if to imply that he rather expected Mr. Winkle's natural taste for perjury would induce him to give some name which did not belong to him.

"Winkle," replied the witness.

"What's your Christian name, sir?" angrily inquired the little judge.

"Nathaniel, sir."

"Daniel—any other name?"

"Nathaniel, sir—my Lord, I mean."

"Nathaniel Daniel, or Daniel Nathaniel?"

"No, my Lord, only Nathaniel—not Daniel at all."

"What did you tell me it was Daniel for, then, sir?" inquired the judge.

"I didn't, my Lord," replied Mr. Winkle.

"You did, sir," replied the judge, with a severe frown. "How could I have got Daniel on my notes, unless you told me so, sir?"

This argument was, of course, unanswerable.

"Mr. Winkle has rather a short memory, my Lord," interposed Mr. Skimpin, with another glance at the jury. "We shall find means to refresh it before we have quite done with him, I dare say."

"You had better be careful, sir," said the little judge, with a sinister look at the witness.

Poor Mr. Winkle bowed, and endeavoured to feign an easiness of manner, which, in his then state of confusion, gave him rather the air of a disconcerted pickpocket.

"Now, Mr. Winkle," said Mr. Skimpin, "attend to me, if you please, sir; and let me recommend you, for your own sake, to bear in mind his Lordship's injunctions to be careful. I believe you are a particular friend of Mr. Pickwick, the defendant, are you not?"

"I have known Mr. Pickwick now, as well as I recollect at this moment, nearly——"

"Pray, Mr. Winkle, do not evade the question. Are you, or are you not, a particular friend of the defendant's?"

"I was just about to say, that——"

"Will you, or will you not, answer my question, sir?"

"If you don't answer the question, you'll be committed, sir," interposed the little judge, looking over his note-book.

"Come, sir," said Mr. Skimpin, "yes or no, if you please."

"Yes, I am," replied Mr. Winkle.

"Yes, you are, and why couldn't you say that at once, sir? Perhaps you know the plaintiff too? Eh, Mr. Winkle?"

"I don't know her; I've seen her."

"Oh, you don't know her, but you've seen her? Now, have the goodness to tell the gentlemen of the jury what you mean by *that*, Mr. Winkle."

"I mean that I am not intimate with her, but I have seen her when I went to call on Mr. Pickwick, in Goswell Street."

"How often have you seen her?"

"How often?"

"Yes, Mr. Winkle, how often? I'll repeat the question for you a dozen times, if you require it, sir." And the learned gentleman, with a firm and steady frown, placed his hands on his hips, and smiled suspiciously to the jury.

On this question arose the edifying brow-beating, customary on such points. First of all, Mr. Winkle said it was quite impossible for him to say how many times he had seen Mrs. Bardell. Then he was asked if he had seen her twenty times, to which he replied, "Certainly—more than that." Then he was asked whether he hadn't seen her a hundred times—whether he couldn't swear that he had seen her more than fifty times—whether he didn't know that he had seen her at least seventy-five times, and so forth; the satisfacory conclusion that was arrived at, at last, being, that he had better take care of himself, and mind what he was about. The witness having been by these means reduced to the requisite ebb of nervous perplexity, the examination was continued as follows—

"Pray, Mr. Winkle, do you remember calling on the defendant Pickwick at these apartments in the plaintiff's house in Goswell Street, on one particular morning, in the month of July last?"

"Yes, I do."

"Were you accompanied on that occasion by a friend of the name of Tupman, and another by the name of Snodgrass?"

"Yes, I was."

"Are they here?"

"Yes, they are," replied Mr. Winkle, looking very earnestly towards the spot where his friends were stationed.

"Pray attend to me, Mr. Winkle, and never mind your friends," said Mr. Skimpin, with another expressive look at the jury. "They must tell their stories without any previous consultation with you, if none has yet taken place (another look at the jury). Now, sir, tell the gentlemen of the jury what you saw on entering the defendant's room on this particular morning. Come; out with it, sir; we must have it, sooner or later."

"The defendant, Mr. Pickwick, was holding the plaintiff in his arms, with his hands clasping her waist," replied Mr. Winkle with natural hesitation, "and the plaintiff appeared to have fainted away."

"Did you hear the defendant say anything?"

"I heard him call Mrs. Bardell a good creature, and I heard him ask her to compose herself, for what a situation it was, if anybody should come, or words to that effect."

"Now, Mr. Winkle, I have only one more question to ask you, and I beg you to bear in mind his Lordship's caution. Will you undertake to swear that Pickwick, the defendant, did not say on the occasion in question—'My dear Mrs. Bardell, you're a good creature; compose yourself to this situation, for to this situation you must come' or words to *that* effect?"

"I—I didn't understand him so, certainly," said Mr. Winkle, astounded at this ingenious dove-tailing of the few words he had heard. "I was on the staircase, and couldn't hear distinctly; the impression on my mind is——"

"The gentlemen of the jury want none of the impressions on your mind, Mr. Winkle, which I fear would be of little service to honest, straightforward men," interposed Mr. Skimpin. "You were on the staircase, and didn't distinctly hear; but you will not swear that Pickwick did not make use of the expressions I have quoted? Do I understand that?"

"No, I will not," replied Mr. Winkle; and down sat Mr. Skimpin with a triumphant countenance.

Mr. Pickwick's case had not gone off in so particularly happy a manner, up to this point, that it could very well afford to have any additional suspicion cast upon it. But as it could afford to be placed in a rather better light, if possible, Mr. Phunky rose for the purpose of getting something important out of

Mr. Winkle in cross-examination. Whether he did get anything important out of him, will immediately appear.

"I believe, Mr. Winkle," said Mr. Phunky, "that Mr. Pickwick is not a young man?"

"Oh, no," replied Mr. Winkle; "old enough to be my father."

"You have told my learned friend that you have known Mr. Pickwick a long time. Had you ever any reason to suppose or believe that he was about to be married?"

"Oh, no; certainly not;" replied Mr. Winkle with so much eagerness, that Mr. Phunky ought to have got him out of the box with all possible despatch. Lawyers hold that there are two kinds of particularly bad witnesses—a reluctant witness, and a too-willing witness; it was Mr. Winkle's fate to figure in both characters.

"I will even go further than this, Mr. Winkle," continued Mr. Phunky, in a most smooth and complacent manner. "Did you ever see anything in Mr. Pickwick's manner and conduct towards the opposite sex, to induce you to believe that he ever contemplated matrimony of late years, in any case?"

"Oh, no; certainly not," replied Mr. Winkle.

"Has his behaviour, when females have been in the case, always been that of a man, who, having attained a pretty advanced period of life, content with his own occupations and amusements, treats them only as a father might his daughters?"

"Not the least doubt of it," replied Mr. Winkle, in the fulness of his heart. "That is—yes—oh, yes—certainly."

"You have never known anything in his behaviour towards Mrs. Bardell, or any other female, in the least degree suspicious?" said Mr. Phunky, preparing to sit down, for Sergeant Snubbin was winking at him.

"N-n-no," replied Mr. Winkle, "except on one trifling occasion, which, I have no doubt, might be easily explained."

Now, if the unfortunate Mr. Phunky had sat down when Sergeant Sunbbin had winked at him, or if Sergeant Buzfuz had stopped this irregular cross-examination at the outset (which he knew better than to do; observing Mr. Winkle's anxiety, and well knowing it would, in all probability, lead to something serviceable to him), this unfortunate admission would not have been elicited. The moment the words fell from Mr. Winkle's lips, Mr. Phunky sat down, and Sergeant Snubbin rather hastily told him he might leave the box, which Mr. Winkle prepared to do with great readiness, when Sergeant Buzfuz stopped him.

"Stay, Mr. Winkle, stay!" said Sergeant Buzfuz, "will your Lordship have the goodness to ask him, what this one instance of suspicious behaviour towards females on the part of this gentleman, who is old enough to be his father, was?"

"You hear what the learned counsel says, sir," observed the judge, turning to the miserable and agonised Mr. Winkle. "Describe the occasion to which you refer."

"My Lord," said Mr. Winkle, trembling with anxiety, "I—I'd rather not."

"Perhaps so," said the little judge, "but you must."

Amid the profound silence of the whole court, Mr.

Winkle faltered out, that the trifling circumstance of suspicion was Mr. Pickwick's being found in a lady's sleeping-apartment at midnight; which had terminated, he believed in the breaking off of the projected marriage of the lady in question, and had led, he knew, to the whole party being forcibly carried before George Nupkins, Esq., magistrate and justice of the peace, for the borough of Ipswich!

"You may leave the box, sir," said Sergeant Snubbin. Mr. Winkle *did* leave the box, and rushed with delirious haste to the George and Vulture, where he was discovered some hours after, by the waiter, groaning in a hollow and dismal manner, with his head buried beneath the sofa cushions.

PICKWICK PAPERS

## AN ARREST FOR MURDER

Mr. Bucket and his fat forefinger are much in consultation together . . . the fat forefinger seems to rise to the dignity of a familiar demon. He puts it to his ears, and it whispers information; he puts it to his lips, and it enjoins him to secrecy; he rubs it over his nose, and it sharpens his scent; he shakes it before a guilty man, and it charms him to his destruction. The Augurs of the Detective Temple invariably predict, that when Mr. Bucket and that finger are in much conference, a terrible avenger will be heard of before long.

Otherwise, mildly studious in his observation of human nature, on the whole a benignant philosopher not disposed to be severe upon the follies of mankind, Mr. Bucket pervades a vast number of houses, and strolls about an infinity of streets: to outward appearance rather languishing for want of an object. He is in the friendliest condition towards his species, and will drink with most of them. He is free with his money, affable in his manners, innocent in his conversation—but, through the placid stream of his life, there glides an undercurrent of forefinger.

* * *

Sir Leicester seems to wake, though his eyes have been wide open; and he looks intently at Mr. Bucket, as Mr. Bucket refers to his watch.

"The party to be apprehended is now in this house," proceeds Mr. Bucket, putting up his watch with a steady hand, and with rising spirits, "and I'm about to take her into custody in your presence. Sir Leicester Dedlock, Baronet, don't you say a word, nor yet stir. There'll be no noise, and no disturbance at all. I'll come back in the course of the evening, if agreeable to you, and endeavour to meet your wishes respecting this unfortunate family matter, and the nobbiest way of keeping it quiet. Now, Sir Leicester Dedlock, Baronet, don't you be nervous on account of the apprehension at present coming off. You shall see the whole case clear, from first to last."

Mr. Bucket rings, goes to the door, briefly whispers Mercury, shuts the door, and stands behind it with his hands folded. After a suspense of a minute or two, the door slowly opens, and a French woman enters. Mademoiselle Hortense.

The moment she is in the room, Mr. Bucket claps the door to, and puts his back against it. The suddenness of the noise occasions her to turn; and then, for the first time, she sees Sir Leicester Dedlock in his chair.

"I ask your pardon," she mutters hurriedly. "They tell me there was no one here."

Her step towards the door brings her front to front with Mr. Bucket. Suddenly a spasm shoots across her face, and she turns deadly pale.

"This is my lodger, Sir Leicester Dedlock," says Mr. Bucket, nodding at her. "This foreign young woman has been my lodger for some weeks back."

"What do Sir Leicester care for that, you think, my angel?" returns Mademoiselle, in a jocular strain.

"Why, my angel," returns Mr. Bucket, "we shall see."

Mademoiselle Hortense eyes him with a scowl upon her tight face, which gradually changes into a smile of scorn. "You are very mysterieuse. Are you drunk?"

"Tolerable sober, my angel," returns Mr. Bucket.

"I come from arriving at this so detestable house with your wife. Your wife have left me, since some minutes. They tell me downstairs that your wife is here. I come here, and your wife is not here. What is the intention of this fool's play, say then?" Mademoiselle demands, with her arms composedly crossed, but with something in her dark cheek beating like a clock.

Mr. Bucket merely shakes the finger at her.

"Ah, my God, you are an unhappy idiot!" cries Mademoiselle, with a toss of her head and a laugh.—"Leave me to pass downstairs, great pig." With a stamp of her foot, and a menace.

"Now, Mademoiselle," says Mr. Bucket, in a cool, determined way, "you go and sit down upon that sofy."

"I will not sit down upon nothing," she replies, with a shower of nods.

"No, Mademoiselle," repeats Mr. Bucket, making no demonstration except with the finger; "you sit down upon that sofy."

"Why?"

"Because I take you into custody on a charge of murder, and you don't need to be told it. Now, I want to be polite to one of your sex and a foreigner, if I can. If I can't, I must be rough: and there's rougher ones outside. What I am to be depends on you. So I recommend you, as a friend, afore another half a blessed moment has passed over your head, to go and sit down upon that sofy."

Mademoiselle complies, saying in a concentrated voice, while that something in her cheek beats fast and hard, "You are a Devil."

"Now, you see," Mr. Bucket proceeds approvingly, "you're comfortable, and conducting yourself as I should expect a foreign young woman of your sense to do. So I'll give you a piece of advice, and it's this. Don't talk too much. You're not expected to say anything here, and you can't keep too quiet a tongue in your head. In short, the less you Parlay, the better, you know." Mr. Bucket is very complacent over this French explanation.

Mademoiselle, with that tigerish expansion of the mouth, and her black eyes darting fire on him, sits upright on the sofa in a rigid state, with her hands clenched—and her feet too, one might suppose—muttering, "Oh, you Bucket, you are a Devil!"

BLEAK HOUSE

## A LITTLE SECRET SERVICE

Mr. Montague being left alone, pondered for some moments, and then said, raising his voice,—

"Is Nadgett in the office there?"

"Here he is, sir." And he promptly entered, shutting the board-room door after him, as carefully as if he were about to plot a murder.

He was the man at a pound a week who made the inquiries. It was no virtue or merit in Nadgett that he transacted all his Anglo-Bengalee business secretly and in the closest confidence; for he was born to be a secret. He was a short, dried-up, withered old man, who seemed to have secreted his very blood; for nobody would have given him credit for the possession of six ounces of it in his whole body. How he lived was a secret; where he lived was a secret; and even what he was, was a secret. In his musty old pocketbook he carried contradictory cards, in some of which he called himself a coal-merchant, in others a wine-merchant, in others a commission-agent, in others a collector, in others an accountant, as if he really didn't know the secret himself. He was always keeping appointments in the City, and the other man never seemed to come. He would sit on 'Change for hours, looking at everybody who walked in and out, and would do the like at Garraway's, and in other business coffee-houses, in some of which he would be occasionally seen drying a very damp pocket-handkerchief before the fire, and still looking over his shoulder for the man who never appeared. He was mildewed, threadbare, shabby; always had flue upon his legs and back; and kept his linen so secret by buttoning up and wrapping over, that he might have had none—perhaps he hadn't. He carried one stained beaver glove, which he dangled before him by the forefinger as he walked or sat; but even its fellow was a secret. . . . He carried bits of sealing-wax and a hieroglyphical old copper seal in his pocket, and often secretly indited letters in corner boxes of the trysting-places before mentioned; but they never appeared to go to anybody, for he would put them into a secret place in his coat, and deliver them to himself weeks afterwards, very much to his own surprise, quite yellow. He was that sort of man that if he had died worth a million of money, or had died worth twopence-halfpenny, everybody would have been perfectly satisfied, and would have said it was just as they expected. And yet he belonged to a class, a race peculiar to the City, who are secrets as profound to one another, as they are to the rest of mankind.

"Mr. Nadgett," said Montague, copying Jonas Chuzzlewit's address upon a piece of paper, from the card which was still lying on the table, "any information about this name, I shall be glad to have myself. Don't you mind what it is. Any you can scrape together, bring me. Bring it to *me*, Mr. Nadgett."

Nadgett put on his spectacles, and read the name attentively; then he looked at the chairman over his glasses, and bowed; then he took them off, and put them in their case; and then put the case in his pocket. When he had done so, he looked, without his spectacles, at the paper as it lay before him, and at the same time produced his pocket-book from somewhere about the middle of his spine. Large as it was, it was very full of documents, but he found a place for this one, and having clasped it carefully, passed it by a kind of solemn legerdemain into the same region as before.

He withdrew with another bow and without a word, opening the door no wider than was sufficient for his passage out, and shutting it as carefully as before. . . .

MARTIN CHUZZLEWIT

## AN UNJUST TRIBUNAL, 1789

Sydney Carton drank nothing but a little coffee, ate some bread, and, having washed and changed to refresh himself, went out to the place of trial.

The court was all astir and a-buzz, when the black sheep—whom many fell away from in dread—pressed him into an obscure corner among the crowd. Mr. Lorry was there, and Dr. Manette was there. She was there, sitting beside her father.

When her husband was brought in, she turned a look upon him, so sustaining, so encouraging, so full of admiring love and pitying tenderness, yet so courageous for his sake, that it called the healthy blood into his face, brightened his glance, and animated his heart. If there had been any eyes to notice the influence of her look on Sydney Carton, it would have been seen to be the same influence exactly.

Before that unjust Tribunal, there was little or no order of procedure, insuring to any accused person any reasonable hearing. There could have been no such Revolution, if all laws, forms and ceremonies had not first been so monstrously abused, that the suicidal vengeance of the Revolution was to scatter them all to the winds.

Every eye was turned to the jury. The same determined patriots and good republicans as yesterday and the day before, and to-morrow and the day after. Eager and prominent among them, one man with a craving face, and his fingers perpetually hovering about his lips, whose appearance gave great satisfaction to the spectators. A life-thirsting, cannibal-looking, bloody minded juryman, the Jacques Three of Saint Antoine. The whole jury, as a jury of dogs impanelled to try the deer.

Every eye then turned to the five judges and the public prosecutor. No favourable leaning in that quarter to-day. A fell, uncompromising, murderous business meaning there. Every eye then sought some other eye in the crowd, and gleamed at it approvingly; and heads nodded at one another, before bending forward with a strained attention.

Charles Evrémonde, called Darnay. Released yesterday. Reaccused and retaken yesterday. Indictment delivered to him last night. Suspected and denounced enemy of Republic, aristocrat, one of a family of tyrants, one of a race proscribed, for that they had used their abolished privileges to the infamous oppression of the people. Charles Evrémonde, called Darnay, in right of such proscription, absolutely dead in law.

To this effect, in as few or fewer words, the public prosecutor.

A TALE OF TWO CITIES

# 5

# *The London Scene*

## CHRISTMAS EVE IN THE CITY

Meanwhile the fog and darkness thickened so, that people ran about with flaring links, proffering their services to go before horses in carriages and conduct them on their way. The ancient tower of a church, whose gruff old bell was always peeping slily down at Scrooge out of a Gothic window in the wall, became invisible, and struck the hours and quarters in the clouds, with tremulous vibrations afterwards, as if its teeth were chattering in its frozen head up there. The cold became intense. In the main street, at the corner of the court, some labourers were repairing the gas-pipes, and had lighted a great fire in a brazier, round which a party of ragged men and boys were gathered, warming their hands and winking their eyes before the blaze in rapture. The water-plug being left in solitude, its overflowings suddenly congealed, and turned to misanthropic ice. The brightness of the shops, where holly sprigs and berries crackled in the lamp heat of the windows, made pale faces ruddy as they passed. Poulterers' and grocers' trades became a splendid joke—a glorious pageant, with which it was next to impossible to believe that such dull principles as bargain and sale had anything to do. The Lord Mayor, in the stronghold of the mighty Mansion House, gave orders to his fifty cooks and butlers to keep Christmas as a Lord Mayor's household should; and even the little tailor, whom he had fined five shillings on the previous Monday for being drunk and bloodthirsty in the streets, stirred up to-morrow's pudding in his garret, while his lean wife and the baby sallied out to buy the beef.

Foggier yet, and colder! Piercing, searching, biting cold. If the good St. Dunstan had but nipped the evil spirit's nose with a touch of such weather as that, instead of using his familiar weapons, then indeed he would have roared to lusty purpose.

CHRISTMAS BOOKS (A CHRISTMAS CAROL)

## AN OASIS OF PEACE

There are still worse places than the Temple, on a sultry day, for basking in the sun, or resting idly in the shade. There is yet a drowsiness in its courts, and a dreamy dullness in its trees and gardens; those who pace its lanes and squares may yet hear the echoes of their footsteps on the sounding stones, and read upon its gates, in passing from the tumult of the Strand or Fleet Street, "Who enters here leaves noise behind." There is still the splash of falling water in fair Fountain Court, and there are yet nooks and corners where dun-haunted students may look down from their dusty garrets, on a vagrant ray of sunlight patching the shade of the tall houses, and seldom troubled to reflect a passing stranger's form. There is yet, in the Temple, something of a clerkly monkish atmosphere, which public offices of law have not disturbed, and even legal firms have failed to scare away. . . .

BARNABY RUDGE

## IMPLACABLE NOVEMBER WEATHER

LONDON. Michaelmas Term lately over, and the Lord Chancellor sitting in Lincoln's Inn Hall. Implacable November weather. As much mud in the streets, as if the waters had but newly retired from the face of the earth, and it would not be wonderful to meet a Megalosaurus, forty feet long or so, waddling like an elephantine lizard up Holborn Hill. Smoke lowering down from the chimney pots, making a soft, black drizzle, with flakes of soot in it as big as full grown snow-flakes—gone into mourning, one might imagine, for the death of the sun. Dogs, undistinguishable in mire. Horses, scarcely better; splashed to their very blinkers. Foot passengers, jostling one another's umbrellas, in a general infection of ill-temper, and losing their foothold at street corners, where tens of thousands of other footpassengers have been slipping and sliding since the day broke (if this day ever broke), adding new deposits to the crust upon crust of mud, sticking at those points tenaciously to the pavement, and accumulating at compound interest.

Fog everywhere. Fog up the river, where it flows among green aits and meadows; fog down the river, where it rolls defiled among the tiers of shipping, and the waterside pollutions of a great (and dirty) city. . . . Chance people on the bridges peeping over the parapets into a nether sky of fog, with fog all round them, as if they were in a balloon, and hanging in the misty clouds.

Gas looming in the fog in divers places in the streets, much as the sun may, from the spongy fields, be seen to loom by husbandman and ploughboy. Most of the shops lighted two hours before their time—as the gas seems to know, for it has a haggard and unwilling look.

The raw afternoon is rawest, and the dense fog is densest, and the muddy streets are muddiest, near that leaden-headed old obstruction, appropriate ornament for the threshold of a leaden-headed old corporation—Temple Bar. And hard by Temple Bar, in Lincoln's Inn Hall, at the very heart of the fog, sits the Lord High Chancellor in his High Court of Chancery.

Never can there come fog too thick, never can there come mud and mire too deep, to assort with the groping and floundering condition which this High Court of Chancery, most pestilent of hoary sinners, holds, this day, in the sight of heaven and earth.

BLEAK HOUSE

## A LONDON PARTICULAR

A young gentleman who had inked himself by accident, addressed me from the pavement, and said, "I am from Kenge and Carboy's, miss, of Lincoln's Inn."

"If you please, sir," said I.

He was very obliging; and as he handed me into a fly, after superintending the removal of my boxes, I asked him whether there was a great fire anywhere? For the streets were so full of dense brown smoke that scarcely anything was to be seen.

"Oh, dear, no, miss," he said. "This is a London particular."

I had never heard of such a thing.

"A fog, miss," said the young gentleman.

"Oh, indeed!" said I.

BLEAK HOUSE

## NOTHING BUT STREETS, STREETS, STREETS

It was a Sunday evening in London, gloomy, close, and stale. Maddening church bells of all degrees of dissonance, sharp and flat, cracked and clear, fast and slow, made the brick-and-mortar echoes hideous. Melancholy streets, in a penitential garb of soot, steeped the souls of the people who were condemned to look at them out of windows, in dire despondency. In every thoroughfare, up almost every alley, and down almost every turning, some doleful bell was throbbing, jerking, tolling, as if the Plague were in the city and the dead-carts were going round. Everything was bolted and barred that could by possibility furnish relief to an over-worked people. . . . Nothing to see but streets, streets, streets. Nothing to breathe but streets, streets, streets. Nothing to change the brooding mind, or raise it up. Nothing for the spent toiler to do, but to compare the monotony of his seventh day with the monotony of his six days, think what a weary life he led and make the best of it—or the worst, according to the probabilities.

LITTLE DORRIT

## THE OLD CURIOSITY SHOP

The place through which he made his way at leisure, was one of these receptacles for old and curious things which seem to crouch in odd corners of this town, and to hide their musty treasures from the public eye in jealousy and distrust. There were suits of mail, standing like ghosts in armour here and there, fantastic carvings brought from monkish cloisters; rusty weapons of various kinds; distorted figures in china, and wood, and iron, and ivory; tapestry and strange furniture that might have been designed in dreams. The haggard aspect of the little old man was wonderfully suited to the place; he might have groped among old churches, and tombs, and deserted houses, and gathered all the spoils with his own hands. There was nothing in the whole collection but was in keeping with himself—nothing that looked older or more worn than he.

As he turned the key in the lock he surveyed me with some astonishment, which was not diminished when he looked from me to my companion. The door being opened, the child addressed him as her grandfather, and told him the little story of our companionship.

"Why, bless thee, child," said the old man, patting her on the head, "how couldst thou miss thy way? What if I had lost thee, Nell?"

"I would have found my way back to *you*, grandfather," said the child boldly; "never fear."

The old man kissed her; then turned to me and begged me to walk in. I did so. The door was closed and locked. Preceding me with the light, he led me through the place I had already seen from without, into a small sitting-room behind, in which was another door opening into a kind of closet, where I saw a little bed, that a fairy might have slept in: it looked so very small and was so prettily arranged. The child took a candle and tripped into this little room, leaving the old man and me together.

"You must be tired, sir," said he, as he placed a chair near the fire; "how can I thank you?"

"By taking more care of your grandchild another time, my good friend," I replied.

"More care!" said the old man, in a shrill voice,

"more care of Nelly! why, who ever loved a child as I love Nell?"

THE OLD CURIOSITY SHOP

## SOHO OF LONG AGO

A quainter corner than the corner where the doctor lived, was not to be found in London. There was no way through it, and the front windows of the doctor's lodgings commanded a pleasant little vista of street that had a congenial air of retirement on it. There were few buildings then, north of the Oxford Road, and forest trees flourished, and wild flowers grew, and the hawthorn blossomed, in the now vanished fields. As a consequence, country airs circulated in Soho with vigorous freedom, instead of languishing into the parish like stray paupers without a settlement; and there was many a good south wall, not far off, on which the peaches ripened in their season.

The summer light struck into the corner brilliantly in the earlier part of the day; but, when the streets grew hot, the corner was in shadow, though not in shadow so remote but that you could see beyond it into a glare of brightness. It was a cool spot, staid but cheerful, a wonderful place for echoes, and a very harbour from the raging streets.

A TALE OF TWO CITIES

# 6

# *To Lie Magnificently*

A MENDACIOUS CABBY

"How old is that horse, my friend?" inquired Mr. Pickwick, rubbing his nose with the shilling he had reserved for the fare.

"Forty-two," replied the driver, eyeing him askant.

"What!" ejaculated Mr. Pickwick, laying his hand upon his note-book. The driver reiterated his former statement. Mr. Pickwick looked very hard at the man's face, but his features were immovable, so he noted down the fact forthwith.

"And how long do you keep him out at a time?" inquired Mr. Pickwick, searching for further information.

"Two or three weeks," replied the man.

"Weeks!" said Mr. Pickwick in astonishment, and out came the note-book again.

"He lives at Pentonwil when he's at home," observed the driver coolly, "but we seldom takes him home, on account of his weakness."

"On account of his weakness!" reiterated the perplexed Mr. Pickwick.

"He always falls down when he's took out of the cab," continued the driver, "but when he's in it, we bears him up werry tight, and takes him in werry short, so as he can't werry well fall down; and we've got a pair of precious large wheels on, so ven he *does* move, they run after him, and he must go on—he can't help it."

PICKWICK PAPERS

## PIP TELLS A NUMBER OF WHOPPERS

"Boy! What like is Miss Havisham?" . . .

"Very tall and dark," I told him.

"Is she, uncle?" asked my sister.

Mr. Pumblechook winked assent; from which I at once inferred that he had never seen Miss Havisham, for she was nothing of the kind.

"Good!" said Mr. Pumblechook, conceitedly. ("This is the way to have him! We are beginning to hold our own, I think, Mum?")

"I am sure, uncle," returned Mrs. Joe, "I wish

you had him always: you know so well how to deal with him."

"Now, boy! what was she a-doing of, when you went in to-day?" asked Mr. Pumblechook.

"She was sitting," I answered, "in a black velvet coach." Mr. Pumblechook and Mrs. Joe stared at one another—as well they might—and both repeated, "In a black velvet coach?"

"Yes," said I. "And Miss Estella—that's her niece, I think—handed her in cake and wine at the coach-window, on a gold plate. And we all had cake and wine on gold plates. And I got up behind the coach to eat mine, because she told me to."

"Was anybody else there?" asked Mr. Pumblechook.

"Four dogs," said I.

"Large or small?"

"Immense," said I. "And they fought for veal cutlets out of a silver basket."

Mr. Pumblechook and Mrs. Joe stared at one another again, in utter amazement. I was perfectly frantic—a reckless witness under the torture—and would have told them anything.

"Where *was* the coach, in the name of gracious?" asked my sister.

"In Miss Havisham's room." They stared again. "But there weren't any horses to it." I added this saving clause, in the moment of rejecting four richly caparisoned coursers which I had wild thoughts of harnessing.

"Can this be possible, uncle?" asked Mrs. Joe. "What can the boy mean?"

"I'll tell you, Mum," said Mr. Pumblechook. "My

opinion is, it's a sedan-chair. She's flighty, you know —very flighty—quite flighty enough to pass her days in a sedan-chair."

"Did you ever see her in it, uncle?" asked Mrs. Joe.

"How could I?" he returned, forced to the admission, "when I never see her in my life? Never clapped eyes upon her!"

"Goodness, uncle! And yet you have spoken to her?"

"Why, don't you know," said Mr. Pumblechook testily, "that when I have been there, I have been took up to the outside of her door, and the door has stood ajar, and she has spoken to me that way. Don't say you don't know *that*, Mum. Howsever, the boy went there to play. What did you play at, boy?"

"We played at flags," I said. (I beg to observe that I think of myself with amazement, when I recall the lies I told on this occasion.)

"Flags!" echoed my sister.

"Yes," said I. "Estella waved a blue flag, and I waved a red one and Miss Havisham waved one sprinkled all over with little gold stars, out at the coach-window. And then we all waved our swords and hurrahed."

"Swords!" repeated my sister. "Where did you get swords from?"

"Out of a cupboard," said I. "And I saw pistols in it—and jam—and pills. And there was no daylight in the room, but it was all lighted up with candles."

"That's true, Mum," said Mr. Pumblechook, with a grave nod. "That's the state of the case, for that much I've seen myself." And then they both stared at me, and I, with an obstrusive show of artlessness on my countenance, stared at them, and plaited the right leg of my trousers with my right hand.

If they had asked me any more questions I should have undoubtedly betrayed myself, for I was even then on the point of mentioning that there was a balloon in the yard, and should have hazarded the statement but for my invention being divided between that phenomenon and a bear in the brewery. They were so much occupied, however, in discussing the marvels I had already presented for their consideration, that I escaped. The subject still held them when Joe came in from his work to have a cup of tea. To whom my sister, more for the relief of her own mind than for the gratification of his, related my pretended experiences. . . .

After Mr. Pumblechook had driven off, and when my sister was washing up, I stole into the forge to Joe, and remained by him until he had done for the night. Then I said, "Before the fire goes out, Joe, I should like to tell you something."

"Should you, Pip?" said Joe, drawing his shoeing-stool near the forge. "Then tell us. What is it, Pip?"

"Joe," said I, taking hold of his rolled-up shirt-sleeve, and twisting it between my finger and thumb, "you remember all that about Miss Havisham's?"

"Remember?" said Joe. "I believe you! Wonderful!"

"It's a terrible thing, Joe; it ain't true."

"What are you telling of, Pip?" cried Joe, falling back in the greatest amazement. "You don't mean to say its——"

"Yes, I do; its lies, Joe."

"But not all of it? why sure you don't mean to say, Pip, that there was no black welwet co—eh?" For I stood shaking my head. "But at least there was dogs, Pip. Come, Pip," said Joe persuasively, "if there warn't no weal-cutlets, at least there was dogs?"

"No, Joe."

"*A* dog?" said Joe. "A puppy? Come?"

"No, Joe, there was nothing at all of the kind."

As I fixed my eyes hopelessly on Joe, Joe contemplated me in dismay. "Pip, old chap! This won't do, old fellow! I say! Where do you expect to go to?"

"It's terrible, Joe; an't it?"

"Terrible?" cried Joe. "Awful! What possessed you?"

"I don't know what possessed me, Joe," I replied, letting his shirt-sleeve go, and sitting down in the ashes at his feet, hanging my head; "but I wish you hadn't taught me to call Knaves at cards, Jacks; and I wish my boots weren't so thick nor my hands so coarse."

And then I told Joe that I felt very miserable and that I hadn't been able to explain myself to Mrs. Joe and Pumblechook who were so rude to me, and that there had been a beautiful young lady at Miss Havisham's who was dreadfully proud, and that she had said I was common, and that the lies had come of it somehow, though I didn't know how.

This was a case of metaphysics, at least as difficult for Joe to deal with as for me. But Joe took the case altogether out of the region of metaphysics and by that means vanquished it.

"There's one thing you may be sure of, Pip," said

Joe after some rumination, "namely, that lies is lies. Howsever they come, they didn't ought to come, and they come from the father of lies, and work round to the same. Don't you tell no more of 'em, Pip. *That* ain't the way to get out of being common, old chap. And as to being common, I don't make it out at all clear. You are oncommon in some things. You're oncommon small. Likewise you're a oncommon scholar."

"No, I am ignorant and backward, Joe."

"Why, see what a letter you wrote last night. Wrote in print even! I've seen letters—Ah! and from gentlefolks!—that I'll swear weren't wrote in print," said Joe.

"I've learnt next to nothing, Joe. You think much of me. It's only that."

"Well, Pip," said Joe, "be it so or be it son't, you must be a common scholar before you can be a oncommon one. I should hope! The king upon his throne, with his crown upon his 'ed, can't sit and write his acts of Parliament in print, without having begun, when he were a unpromoted Prince, with the alphabet—Ah!" added Joe, with a shake of the head that was full of meaning, "and begun with A too, and worked his way to Z. And *I* know what that is to do, though I can't say I've exactly done it. . . ." "Lookee here, Pip, at what is said to you by a true friend. Which this to you the true friend say. If you can't get to be oncommon through going straight, you'll never get to do it through going crooked. So don't tell no more on 'em, Pip, and live well and die happy."

GREAT EXPECTATIONS

## BELIEVE IT OR BELIEVE IT NOT

"Fine pursuit, sir—fine pursuit—Dogs, sir?"

"Not just now," said Mr. Winkle.

"Ah! you should keep dogs—fine animals—sagacious creatures—dog of my own once—pointer—surprising instinct—out shooting one day—entering inclosure—whistled—dog stopped—whistled again—Ponto—no go; stock still—called him—Ponto, Ponto—wouldn't move—dog transfixed—staring at a board—looked up, saw an inscription—'Gamekeeper has orders to shoot all dogs found in this inclosure'—wouldn't pass it—wonderful dog—valuable dog that—very."

"Singular circumstance that," said Mr. Pickwick. "Will you allow me to make a note of it?"

PICKWICK PAPERS

# 7

# *A Little Learning*

## PAUL DOMBEY WANTS TO KNOW

But it was generally said that Mrs. Pipchin was a woman of system with children; and no doubt she was. Certainly the wild ones went home tame enough, after sojourning for a few months beneath her hospitable roof. It was generally said, too, that it was highly creditable of Mrs. Pipchin to have devoted herself to this way of life, and to have made such a sacrifice of her feelings, and such a resolute stand against her troubles, when Mr. Pipchin broke his heart in the Peruvian mines.

At this exemplary old lady, Paul would sit staring in his little arm-chair by the fire, for any length of time. He never seemed to know what weariness was when he was looking fixedly at Mrs. Pipchin. He was not fond of her; he was not afraid of her; but in those old, old moods of his, she seemed to have a grotesque attraction for him. There he would sit, looking at her, and warming his hands, and looking at her, until he sometimes quite confounded Mrs. Pipchin, Ogress as she was. Once she asked him, when they were alone, what he was thinking about.

"You," said Paul, without the least reserve.

"And what are you thinking about me?" asked Mrs. Pipchin.

"I'm thinking how old you must be," said Paul.

"You must'nt say such things as that, young gentleman," returned the dame. "That'll never do."

"Why not?" asked Paul.

"Because it's not polite," said Mrs. Pipchin snappishly.

"Not polite?" asked Paul.

"No."

"It's not polite," said Paul innocently, "to eat all the mutton-chops and toast, Wickam says."

"Wickam," retorted Mrs. Pipchin, colouring, "is a wicked, impudent, bold-faced hussy."

"What's that?" inquired Paul.

"Never you mind, sir," retorted Mrs. Pipchin. "Remember the story of the little boy that was gored to death by a mad bull for asking questions."

"If the bull was mad," said Paul, "how did *he*

know that the boy had asked questions? Nobody can go and whisper secrets to a mad bull. I don't believe that story."

"You don't believe it, sir?" repeated Mrs. Pipchin, amazed.

"No," said Paul.

"Not if it should happen to have been a tame bull, you little infidel?" said Mrs. Pipchin.

As Paul had not considered the subject in that light, and had founded his conclusions on the alleged lunacy of the bull, he allowed himself to be put down for the present. But he sat turning it over in his mind, with such an obvious intention of fixing Mrs. Pipchin presently, that even that hardy old lady deemed it prudent to retreat until he should have forgotten the subject.

DOMBEY AND SON

## FACTS SIR, NOTHING BUT FACTS

"Now, what I want is, Facts. Teach these boys and girls nothing but Facts. Facts alone are wanted in life. Plant nothing else, and root out everything else. You can only form the minds of reasoning animals upon Facts: nothing else will ever be of any service to them. This is the principle on which I bring up my own children, and this is the principle on which I bring up these children. Stick to Facts, sir!"

The scene was a plain, bare, monotonous vault of a school-room, and the speaker's square forefinger emphasised his observations by underscoring every sentence with a line on the schoolmaster's sleeve. The emphasis was helped by the speaker's square wall of a forehead, which had his eyebrows for its base, while his eyes found commodious cellarage in two dark caves, overshadowed by the wall. The emphasis was helped by the speaker's mouth, which was wide, thin, and hard set. The emphasis was helped by the speaker's voice, which was inflexible, dry, and dictatorial. The emphasis was helped by the speaker's hair, which bristled on the skirts of his bald head, a plantation of firs to keep the wind from its shining surface, all covered with knobs, like the crust of a plum pie, as if the head had scarcely warehouse-room for the hard facts stored inside. The speaker's obstinate carriage, square coat, square legs, square shoulders—nay, his very neckcloth, trained to take him by the throat with an unaccommodating grasp, like a stubborn fact, as it was, all helped the emphasis.

"In this life, we want nothing but Facts, sir—nothing but Facts!"

HARD TIMES

## AT DOTHEBOYS HALL

After some half-hour's delay, Mr. Squeers reappeared, and the boys took their places and their books, of which latter commodity the average might be about one to eight learners. A few moments having elapsed, during which Mr. Squeers looked very profound, as if he had a perfect apprehension of what was inside all the books, and could say every word of their contents by heart if he only chose to take the trouble, that gentleman called up the first class.

Obedient to this summons there ranged themselves in front of the schoolmaster's desk, half-a-dozen scarecrows, out at knees and elbows, one of whom placed a torn and filthy book beneath his learned eye.

"This is the first class in English spelling and philosophy, Nickleby," said Squeers, beckoning Nicholas to stand beside him, "We'll get up a Latin one, and hand that over to you. Now, then, where's the first boy?"

"Please, sir, he's cleaning the back parlour window," said the temporary head of the philosophical class.

"So he is, to be sure," rejoined Squeers. "We go upon the practical mode of teaching, Nickleby; the regular education system. C-l-e-a-n, clean, verb active, to make bright, to scour. W-i-n, win, d-e-r, der, winder, a casement. When the boy knows this out of the book, he goes and does it. It's just the same principle as the use of the globes. "Where's the second boy?"

"Please, sir, he's weeding the garden," replied a small voice. "To be sure," said Squeers, by no means disconcerted. "So he is. B-o-t, bot, t-i-n, tin, bottin n-e-y, bottinney, noun substantive, a knowledge of plants. When he has learned that bottinney means a knowledge of plants he goes and knows 'em. That's our system, Nickleby; what do you think of it?"

"It's a very useful one, at any rate," answered Nicholas.

"I believe you," rejoined Squeers, not remarking the emphasis of his usher. "Third boy, what's a horse?"

"A beast, sir," replied the boy.

"So it is," said Squeers. "Ain't it Nickleby?"

"I believe there is no doubt of that, sir," answered Nicholas.

"Of course there isn't," said Squeers. "A horse is a quadruped, and quadruped's Latin for beast, as everybody that's gone through the grammar knows, or else where's the use of having grammars at all?"

"Where, indeed!" said Nicholas abstractedly.

"As you're perfect in that," resumed Squeers, turning to the boy, "go and look after my horse, and rub him down well, or I'll rub you down. The rest of the class go and draw water up, till somebody tells you to leave off, for it's washing-day to-morrow and they want the coppers filled."

So saying, he dismissed the first class to their experiments in practical philosophy, and eyed Nicholas with a look, half cunning and half doubtful, as if were not altogether certain what he might think of him by this time.

NICHOLAS NICKLEBY

## MR. BAPTIST LEARNS SOME ENGLISH

The foreigner, by name John Baptist Cavalletto—they called him Mr. Baptist in the Yard—was such a chirping, easy, hopeful little fellow. . . . Solitary, weak, and scantily acquainted with the most necessary words of the only language in which he could communicate with the people about him, he went with the stream of his fortunes, in a brisk way that was new in those parts. With little to eat, and less to drink, and nothing to wear but what he wore upon him, or had brought tied up in one of the smallest bundles that ever were seen, he put as bright a face upon it as if he were in the most flourishing circumstances, when he first hobbled up and down the Yard, humbly propitiating the general good-will with his white teeth.

It was up-hill work for a foreigner, lame or sound, to make his way with the Bleeding Hearts. In the first place, they were vaguely persuaded that every foreigner had a knife about him; in the second, they held it to be a sound constitutional national axiom that he ought to go home to his own country. . . .

. . . However, the Bleeding Hearts were kind hearts; and when they saw the little fellow cheerily limping about with a good-humoured face, doing no harm, drawing no knives, committing no outrageous immoralities, living chiefly on farinaceous and milk diet, and playing with Mrs. Plornish's children of an evening, they began to think that although he could never hope to be an Englishman, still it would be hard to visit that affliction on his head. They began to accommodate themselves to his level, calling him "Mr. Baptist," but treating him like a baby, and laughing immoderately at his lively gestures and his childish English—more, because he didn't mind it, and laughed too. They spoke to him in very loud voices as if he were stone deaf. They constructed sentences, by way of teaching the language in its purity, such as were addressed by the savages to Captain Cook, or by Friday to Robinson Crusoe. Mrs. Plornish was particularly ingenious in this art; and attained so much celebrity by saying "Me ope you leg well soon," that it was considered in the Yard but a very short remove indeed from speaking Italian. Even Mrs. Plornish herself began to think that she had a natural call towards that language. As he became more popular, household objects were brought into requisition for his instruction in a copious vocabulary; and whenever he appeared in the Yard ladies would fly out at their doors crying "Mr. Baptist—tea-pot!" "Mr. Baptist—dust-pan!" "Mr. Baptist—flour-dredger!" "Mr. Baptist—coffee-biggin!" At the same time exhibiting those articles, and penetrating him with a sense of the appalling difficulties of the Anglo-Saxon tongue.

LITTLE DORRIT

## A MIRACLE OF ERUDITION

Mr. Wopsle's great-aunt kept an evening school in the village; that is to say, she was a ridiculous old woman of limited means and unlimited infirmity, who used to go to sleep from six to seven every evening, in the society of youth who paid twopence per week each for the improving opportunity of seeing her do it. . . .

Much of my unassisted self, and more by the help of Biddy than of Mr. Wopsle's great-aunt, I struggled through the alphabet as if it had been a bramble-bush; getting considerably worried and scratched by every letter. After that, I fell among those thieves, the nine figures, who seemed every evening to do something new to disguise themselves and baffle recognition. But, at last I began, in a purblind, groping way, to read, write, and cipher on the very smallest scale.

One night, I was sitting in the chimney-corner with my slate, expending great efforts on the production of a letter to Joe. I think it must have been a full year after our hunt upon the marshes, for it was a long time after, and it was winter and a hard frost. With an alphabet on the hearth at my feet for reference, I contrived in an hour or two to print and smear this epistle:—

"mI deEr JO i opE U r krWitE wEll i opE i shAl soN B haBelL 4 2 TeeDge U JO aN theN wE shOrl b sO glOdd aN wEn i M preNgtD 2 u JO woT larX an blEvE ME inF xn PiP."

There was no indispensable necessity for my communicating with Joe by letter, inasmuch as he sat beside me and we were alone. But I delivered this written communication (slate and all) with my own hand, and Joe received it as a miracle of erudition.

"I say, Pip, old chap!" cried Joe, opening his blue eyes wide, "what a scholar you are. An't you?"

GREAT EXPECTATIONS

## THE FORCING HOUSE OF DR. BLIMBER

Whenever a young gentleman was taken in hand by Dr. Blimber, he might consider himself sure of a pretty tight squeeze. The Doctor only undertook the charge of ten young gentlemen, but he had, always ready, a supply of learning for a hundred, on the lowest estimate; and it was at once the business and delight of his life to gorge the unhappy ten with it.

In fact, Dr. Blimber's establishment was a great hothouse, in which there was a forcing apparatus incessantly at work. All the boys blew before their time. Mental green peas were produced at Christmas, and intellectual asparagus all the year round. Mathematical gooseberries (very sour ones too) were common at untimely seasons, and from mere sprouts of bushes, under Doctor Blimber's cultivation. Every description of Greek and Latin vegetable was got off the driest twigs of boys, under the frostiest circumstances. Nature was of no consequence at all. No matter what a young gentleman was intended to bear, Doctor Blimber made him bear to pattern, somehow or other.

This was all very pleasant and ingenious, but the system of forcing was attended with its usual disadvantages. There was not the right taste about the premature productions, and they didn't keep well. Moreover, one young gentleman, with a swollen nose and an excessively large head (the oldest of the ten who had 'gone through' everything), suddenly left off blowing one day, and remained in the establishment a mere stalk. And people did say that the Doctor had rather overdone it with young Toots, and that when he began to have whiskers he left off having brains.

DOMBEY AND SON

## MR. PODSNAP INSTRUCTS A FOREIGN GENTLEMAN

The majority of the guests were like the plate, and included several heavy articles weighing ever so much. But there was a foreign gentleman among them: whom Mr. Podsnap had invited after much debate with himself . . . and there was a droll disposition, not only on the part of Mr. Podsnap, but of everybody else, to treat him as if he were a child who was hard of hearing.

As a delicate concession to this unfortunately-born foreigner, Mr. Podsnap, in receiving him, had presented his wife as "Madame Podsnap," also his daughter as "Mademoiselle Podsnap," with some inclination to add "ma fille," in which bold venture, however, he checked himself. The Veneerings being at that time the only other arrivals, he had added (in a condescendingly explanatory manner), "Monsieur Vey-nair-reeng," and had then subsided into English.

"How do you like London?" Mr. Podsnap now inquired from his station as host, as if he were administering something in the nature of a powder or potion to the deaf child; "London, Londres, London?"

The foreign gentleman admired it.

"You find it Very Large?" said Mr. Podsnap, spaciously.

The foreign gentleman found it very large.

"And Very Rich?"

The foreign gentleman found it, without doubt, enormément riche.

"Enormously Rich, we say," returned Mr. Podsnap, in a condescending manner. "Our English adverbs do Not terminate in Mong, and We Pronounce the 'ch' as if there was a 't' before it. We Say Ritch."

"Reetch," remarked the foreign gentleman.

"And Do You Find, Sir," pursued Mr. Podsnap, with dignity, "Many Evidences that Strike You, of our British Constitution in the Streets Of The World's Metropolis, London, Londres, London?" The foreign gentleman begged to be pardoned, but did not altogether understand.

"The Constitution Britannique," Mr. Podsnap explained, as if he were teaching in an infant school. "We Say British, But You Say Britannique. You

Know" (forgivingly, as if that were not his fault), "The Constitution, Sir."

The foreign gentleman said, "Mais, yees; I know eem."

A youngish sallowish gentleman in spectacles, with a lumpy forehead, seated in a supplementary chair at a corner of the table, here caused a profound sensation by saying, in a raised voice, "ESKER," and then stopped dead.

"Mais oui," said the foreign gentleman, turning towards him. "Est-ce que? Quoi donc?"

But the gentleman with the lumpy forehead having for the time delivered himself of all that he found behind his lumps, spake for the time no more.

"I Was Inquiring," said Mr. Podsnap, resuming the thread of his discourse, "Whether You Have Observed in our Streets as We should say, Upon our Pavvy as You would say, any Tokens——" The foreign gentleman with patient courtesy entreated pardon; "But what was tokenz?"

"Marks," said Mr. Podsnap; "Signs, you know, Appearances—Traces."

"Ah! Of a Orse?" inquired the foreign gentleman.

"We call it Horse," said Mr. Podsnap, with forbearance. In England, Angleterre, England, We Aspirate the 'H', and We Say 'Horse', Only our Lower Classes Say 'Orse!' "

"Pardon," said the foreign gentleman; "I am alwiz wrong!"

"Our Language," said Mr. Podsnap, with a gracious consciousness of being always right, "is Difficult. Ours is a Copious Language, and Trying to Strangers. I will not Pursue my Question."

But the lumpy gentleman, unwilling to give it up, again madly said "ESKER," and again spake no more.

"It merely referred," Mr. Podsnap explained, with a sense of meritorious proprietorship, "to Our Constitution, Sir. We Englishmen are Very Proud of Our Constitution, Sir. It Was Bestowed Upon Us By Providence. No Other Country is so Favoured as This Country."

"And ozer countries?—" the foreign gentleman was beginning, when Mr. Podsnap put him right again.

"We do not say Ozer; we say Other: the letters are 'T' and 'H'; you say Tay and Aish, You know" (still with clemency). The sound is 'th'—'th!' "

"And *other* countries," said the foreign gentleman. "They do how?"

"They do, Sir," returned Mr. Podsnap, gravely shaking his head; "They do—I am sorry to be obliged to say it—*as* they do."

"It was a little particular of Providence," said the foreign gentleman, laughing; "for the frontier is not large."

"Undoubtedly," assented Mr. Podsnap; "But So it is. It was the Charter of the Land. This Island was Blessed, Sir, to the Direct Exclusion of such Other Countries as—as there may happen to be. And if we were all Englishmen present, I would say," added Mr. Podsnap, looking round upon his compatriots, and sounding solemnly with his theme, "that there is in the Englishman a combination of qualities, a modesty, an independence, a responsibility, a repose, combined with an absence of everything calculated to call a blush into the cheek of a young person, which one would seek in vain among the Nations of the Earth."

OUR MUTUAL FRIEND

## A QUEST FOR GREEK ROOTS

Doctor Strong's was an excellent school; as different from Mr. Creakle's as good is from evil. It was very gravely and decorously ordered, and on a sound system; with an appeal, in everything, to the honour and good faith of the boys. . . . Some of the higher scholars boarded in the Doctor's house, and through them I learned, at second hand, some particulars of the Doctor's history . . . how the Doctor's cogitating manner was attributable to his always being engaged in looking out for Greek roots; which, in my innocence and ignorance, I supposed to be a botanical furor on the Doctor's part, especially as he always looked at the ground when he walked about, until I understood that they were roots of words, with a view to a new dictionary which he had in contemplation. Adams, our head-boy, who had a turn for mathematics, had made a calculation, I was informed, of the time this Dictionary would take in completing, on the Doctor's plan, and at the Doctor's rate of going. He considered that it might be done in one thousand six hundred and forty-nine years, counting from the Doctor's last, or sixty-second, birthday.

DAVID COPPERFIELD

# 8

# *Essays in Invective*

## THE UNMASKING OF A PATRIACH

*(Mr. Pancks, collector of rents in Bleeding Heart Yard for Christopher Casby, a hoary-headed old humbug with a patriachal air, meets his employer among the tenants shortly after having been accused of not squeezing them enough.)*

The Patriach, approaching with his usual benignity, was surprised to see Mr. Pancks, but supposed him to have been stimulated to an immediate squeeze instead of postponing that operation until Monday. The population of the Yard were astonished at the meeting, for the two powers had never been there together, within the memory of the oldest Bleeding Heart. But they were overcome by the unutterable amazement when Mr. Pancks, going close to the most venerable of men, and halting in front of the bottle-green waistcoat, made a trigger of his right thumb and forefinger, applied the same to the brim of the broad-brimmed hat, and, with singular smartness and precision, shot it off the polished head as if it had been a large marble.

Having taken this little liberty with the Patriachal person, Mr. Pancks further astounded and attracted the Bleeding Hearts by saying in an audible voice, "Now, you sugary swindler, I mean to have it out with you!"

Mr. Pancks and the Patriach were instantly the centre of a press, all eyes and ears; windows were thrown open, and doorsteps were thronged.

"What do you pretend to be?" said Mr. Pancks. "What's your moral game? What do you go in for? Benevolence, an't it? You benevolent!" Here Mr. Pancks, apparently without the intention of hitting him, but merely to relieve his mind and expend his superfluous power in wholesome exercise, aimed a blow at the bumpy head, which the bumpy head ducked to avoid. This singular performance was repeated, to the ever-increasing admiration of the spectators, at the end of every succeeding article of Mr. Panck's oration.

"I have discharged myself from your service," said

Pancks, "that I may tell you what you are. You're one of a lot of impostors that are the worst lot of all the lots to be met with. . . . You're a driver in disguise, a screwer by deputy, a wringer, and squeezer, and a shaver by substitute. You're a philanthropic sneak. You're a shabby deceiver!"

(The repetition of the performance at this point was received with a burst of laughter.)

"Ask these good people who's the hard man here. They'll tell you Pancks, I believe."

This was confirmed with cries of "Certainly," and "Hear!"

"But I tell you, good people—Casby! This mound of meekness, this lump of love, this bottle-green smiler, this is your driver," said Pancks. "If you want to see the man who would flay you alive—here he is! Don't look for him in me, at thirty shillings a week, but look for him in Casby, at I don't know how much a year!"

"Good!" cried several voices. "Hear Mr. Pancks!"

"Hear Mr. Pancks?" cried that gentleman (after repeating the popular performance). "Yes, I should think so! It's almost time to hear Mr. Pancks. Mr. Pancks has come down into the Yard to-night on purpose that you should hear him. Pancks is only the Works; but here is the Winder!"

The audience would have gone over to Mr. Pancks as one man, woman and child, but for the long, grey, silken locks and the broad-brimmed hat.

"Here's the Stop," said Pancks, "that sets the tune to be ground. And there is but one tune, and its name is Grind, Grind, Grind! Here's the Proprietor, and here's his Grubber. Why, good people, when he comes smoothly spinning through the Yard to-night, like a slow-going benevolent Humming-Top, and when you come about him with your complaints of the Grubber, you don't know what a cheat the Proprietor is! What do you think of his showing himself to-night, that I may have all the blame on Monday? What do you think of his having had me over the coals this very evening because I don't squeeze you enough? What do you think of my being, at the present moment, under special orders to squeeze you dry on Monday? . . . Here is your benevolent Patriach of a Casby. . . . He is uncommonly improving to look at, and I am not at all so. He is as sweet as honey, and I am as dull as ditch-water. He provides the pitch, and I handle it, and it sticks to me. Now," said Mr. Pancks, closing upon his late proprietor again, from whom he had withdrawn a little for the better display of him to the Yard; "as I am not accustomed to speak in public, and as I have made a rather lengthy speech, all circumstances considered, I shall bring my observations to a close by requesting you to get out of this."

The last of the Patriachs had been so seized by assault, and required so much room to catch an idea in, and so much more room to turn it in, that he had not a word to offer in reply. He appeared to be meditating some Patriachal way out of his delicate position, when Mr. Pancks, once more suddenly applying the trigger to his hat, shot it off again with his former dexterity. On the preceding occasion, one or two of the Bleeding Heart Yarders had obsequiously picked it up and handed it to its owner; but Mr.

Pancks had now so far impressed his audience, that the Patriach had to turn and stoop for it himself.

Quick as lightning, Mr. Pancks, who for some moments had had his right hand in his coat pocket, whipped out a pair of shears, swooped upon the Patriach behind, and snipped off short the sacred locks that flowed upon his shoulders. In a paroxysm of animosity and rapidity, Mr. Pancks then caught the broad-brimmed hat out of the astounded Patriach's hand, cut it down into a mere stewpan, and fixed it on the Patriach's head.

Before the frightful results of this desperate action, Mr. Pancks himself recoiled in consternation. A bare-polled, goggle-eyed, big-headed lumbering personage stood staring at him, not in the least impressive, not in the least venerable, who seemed to have started out of the earth to ask what had become of Casby. . . . Mr. Pancks deemed it prudent to use all possible dispatch in making off, though he was pursued by nothing but the sound of laughter in Bleeding Heart Yard, rippling through the air, and making it ring again.

LITTLE DORRIT

## SOME HOME TRUTHS FOR MR. PECKSNIFF

"Do you threaten me, sir?" cried Mr. Pecksniff.

Martin looked at him, and made no answer; but a curious observer might have detected an ominous twitching at his mouth, and perhaps an involuntary attraction of his right hand in the direction of Mr. Pecksniff's cravat.

"I lament to be obliged to say, sir," resumed Mr.

Pecksniff, "that it would be quite in keeping with your character if you did threaten me. You have deceived me. You have imposed upon a nature which you know to be confiding and unsuspicious. You have obtained admission, sir," said Mr. Pecksniff, rising, "to this house on perverted statements, and on false pretences."

"Go on," said Martin, with a scornful smile. "I understand you now. What more?"

"Thus much more, sir," cried Mr. Pecksniff, trembling from head to foot, and trying to rub his hands, as though he were only cold. "Thus much more, if you force me to publish your shame before a third party, which I was unwilling and indisposed to do. This lowly roof, sir, must not be contaminated by the presence of one who has deceived, and cruelly deceived, an honourable, beloved, venerated, and venerable gentleman; and who wisely suppressed that deceit from me when he sought my protection and favour, knowing that, humble as I am, I am an honest man, seeking to do my duty in this carnal universe, and setting my face against all vice and treachery. I weep for your depravity, sir," said Mr. Pecksniff; "I mourn over your corruption, I pity your voluntary withdrawal of yourself from the flowery paths of purity and peace;" here he struck himself upon his breast, or moral garden; "but I cannot have a leper and a serpent for an inmate. Go forth," said Mr. Pecksniff, stretching out his hand; "go forth, young man! Like all who know you, I renounce you!"

With what intention Martin made a stride forward at these words it is impossible to say. It is enough to know that Tom Pinch caught him in his arms, and that, at the same moment, Mr. Pecksniff stepped back so hastily that he missed his footing, tumbled over a chair, and fell in a sitting posture on the ground; where he remained without an effort to get up again, with his head in a corner, perhaps considering it the safest place.

"Let me go, Pinch!" cried Martin, shaking him away. "Why do you hold me? Do you think a blow could make him a more abject creature than he is? Do you think that if I spat upon him, I could degrade him to a lower level than his own? Look at him. Look at him, Pinch!" . . .

"I tell you," said Martin, "that as he lies there, disgraced, bought, used; a cloth for dirty hands, a mat for dirty feet, a lying, fawning, servile hound; he is the very last and worst among the vermin of the world. And mark me, Pinch! The day will come—he knows it; see it written on his face while I speak! —when even you will find out, and will know him as I do, and as he knows I do. *He* renounce me! Cast your eyes on the renouncer, Pinch, and be the wiser for the recollection!"

He pointed at him as he spoke with unutterable contempt, and, flinging his hat upon his head, walked from the room and from the house.

MARTIN CHUZZLEWIT

## THE ELOQUENCE OF MR. SMALLWEED

The trooper . . . lights his pipe and drinks to Mr. Smallweed's friend in the city—the one solitary flight of that esteemed old gentleman's imagination.

"So you think he might be hard on me, eh?"

"I think he might—I am afraid he would. I have known him do it," says Grandfather Smallweed incautiously, "twenty times."

Incautiously, because his stricken better-half, who has been dozing over the fire for some time, is instantly aroused and jabbers "Twenty thousand pounds, twenty twenty pound notes in a money box, twenty guineas, twenty million, twenty per cent. twenty——" and is then cut short by the flying cushion, which the visitor, to whom this singular experience appears to be a novelty, snatches from her face as it crushes her in the usual manner.

"You're a brimstone idiot. You're a scorpion—a brimstone scorpion! You're a sweltering toad. You're a chattering, clattering broomstick witch, that ought to be burnt!" gasps the old man, prostrate in his chair. "My dear friend, will you shake me up a little?"

* * *

". . . I am speaking of your brother, you brimstone black-beetle, that was seventy-six years of age."

Mrs. Smallwood instantly begins to shake her head, and pipe up, "Seventy-six pound seven and sevenpence! Seventy-six thousand bags of money! Seventy-six hundred thousand million of parcels of bank notes!"

"Will somebody give me a quart pot?" exclaims her exasperated husband, looking helplessly about him, and finding no missile within his reach. "Will somebody obleege me with a spitoon? Will somebody hand me anything hard and bruising to pelt at her? You hag, you cat, you dog, you brimstone barker!" Here Mr. Smallweed, wrought up to the highest pitch by his own eloquence, actually throws Judy at her grandmother in default of anything else, by butting that young virgin at the old lady with such force as he can muster, and then dropping into his chair in a heap.

BLEAK HOUSE

## AN EDITOR LETS HIMSELF GO

. . . Mr. Pott, drawing forth the last number of the *Eatanswill Gazette*, and referring to the same, delivered himself of the following paragraph:

"HOLE-AND-CORNER BUFFERY

"A reptile contemporary has recently sweltered forth his black venom in the vain and hopeless attempt of sullying the fair name of our distinguished and excellent representative, the Honourable Mr. Slumkey—the Slumkey whom we, long before he gained his present noble and exalted position, predicted would one day be, as he now is, his country's brightest honour, and her proudest boast: alike her bold defender and her honest pride—our reptile contemporary, we say, has made himself merry, at the expense of a superbly embossed plated coal-scuttle, which has been presented to that glorious man by his enraptured constituents; and towards the purchase of which, the nameless wretch insinuates, the Honourable Mr. Slumkey himself contributed, through a confidential friend of his butler's, more than three-fourths of the whole sum subscribed. Why, does not this crawling creature see, that even if this be the fact, the Honourable Mr. Slumkey only appears in a still more amiable and radiant light than before, if that be possible? Does not even his obtuseness perceive that this amiable and touching desire to carry out the wishes of the constituent body, must for ever endear him to the hearts and souls of such of his fellow townsmen as are not worse than swine; or, in other words, who are not as debased as our contemporary himself? But such is the wretched trickery of hole-and-corner Buffery! These are not its only artifices. Treason is abroad. We boldly state, now that we are goaded to the disclosure, and we throw ourselves on the country and its constables for protection—we boldly state that secret preparations are at this moment in progress for a Buff ball; which is to be held in a Buff town, in the very heart and centre of a Buff population; which is to be conducted by a Buff master of the ceremonies; which is to be attended by four ultra Buff members of Parliament, and the admission to which, is to be by Buff tickets! Does our fiendish contemporary wince? Let him writhe, in impotent malice, as we pen the words, WE WILL BE THERE."

"There, sir," said Pott, folding up the paper quite exhausted, "that is the state of the case!"

PICKWICK PAPERS

# 9

# *Some Observations on Food*

A MOST OBLIGING WAITER

. . . When the waiter laid a cloth on purpose for me, and put a set of casters on it, I think I must have turned red all over with modesty.

He brought me some chops and vegetables, and took the covers off in such a bouncing manner that I was afraid I must have given him some offence. But he greatly relieved my mind by putting a chair for me at the table, and saying very affably, "Now, six-foot! come on!"

I thanked him, and took my seat at the board; but found it extremely difficult to handle my knife and fork with anything like dexterity, or to avoid splashing myself with the gravy, while he was standing opposite, staring so hard, and making me blush in the most dreadful manner every time I caught his eye. After watching me into the second chop, he said:

"There's half a pint of ale for you. Will you have it now?"

I thanked him and said "Yes." Upon which he poured it out of a jug into a large tumbler, and held it up against the light, and made it look beautiful.

"My eye!" he said. "It seems a good deal, don't it?"

"It does seem a good deal," I answered with a smile. For it was quite delightful to me to find him so pleasant. He was a twinkling-eyed, pimple-faced man, with his hair standing upright all over his head; and as he stood with one arm akimbo, holding up the glass to the light with the other hand, he looked quite friendly.

"There was a gentleman here yesterday," he said—"a stout gentleman, by the name of Topsawyer—perhaps you know him?"

"No," I said, "I don't think——"

"In breeches and gaiters, broad-brimmed hat, grey coat, speckled choker," said the waiter.

"No," I said bashfully, "I haven't the pleasure——"

"He came in here," said the waiter, looking at the light through the tumbler, "ordered a glass of this ale—*would* order it—I told him not—drank it, and fell dead. It was too old for him. It oughtn't to be drawn; that's the fact."

I was very much shocked to hear of this melancholy accident, and said I thought I had better have some water.

"Why, you see," said the waiter, still looking at the light through the tumbler, with one of his eyes shut up, "our people don't like things being ordered and left. It offends 'em. But *I'll* drink it, if you like. I'm used to it, and use is everything. I don't think it'll hurt me, if I throw my head back, and take it off quick. Shall I?"

I replied that he would much oblige me by drinking it, if he thought he could do it safely, but by no means otherwise. When he did throw his head back, and take it off quick, I had a horrible fear, I confess, of seeing him meet the fate of the lamented Mr. Topsawyer, and fall lifeless on the carpet, but it didn't hurt him. On the contrary, I thought he seemed the fresher for it.

"What have we got here?" he said, putting a fork into my dish. "Not chops?"

"Chops," I said.

"Lord bless my soul," he exclaimed. "I didn't know they were chops. Why a chop's the very thing to take off the bad effects of that beer! Ain't it lucky?"

So he took a chop by the bone in one hand, and a potato in the other, and ate away with a very good appetite, to my extreme satisfaction. He afterwards took another chop, and another potato; and after that another chop and another potato. When he had done, he brought me a pudding, and having set it before me, seemed to ruminate, and to become absent in his mind for some moments.

"How's the pie?" he said, rousing himself.

"It's a pudding," I made answer.

"Pudding!" he exclaimed. "Why, bless me, so it is! What!" looking at it nearer. "You don't mean to say it's a batter-pudding?"

"Yes, it is indeed."

"Why, a batter-pudding," he said, taking up a table-spoon, "is my favourite pudding! Ain't that lucky? Come on, little 'un, and let's see who'll get most."

The waiter certainly got most. He entreated me more than once to come in and win, but what with his table-spoon to my tea-spoon, his dispatch to my dispatch, and his appetite to my appetite, I was left far behind at the first mouthful, and had no chance with him. I never saw anyone enjoy a pudding so much, I think; and he laughed, when it was all gone, as if his enjoyment of it lasted still.

DAVID COPPERFIELD

## WHO EATS TRIPE?

"This is a description of animal food, Alderman," said Filer, making little punches in it, with a pencil-case, "commonly known to the labouring population of this country, by the name of tripe."

The Alderman laughed, and winked; for he was a merry fellow, Alderman Cute. Oh, and a sly fellow, too! A knowing fellow. Up to everything. Not to be imposed upon. Deep in the people's hearts! He knew them, Cute did. I believe you!

"But who eats tripe?" said Mr. Filer, looking round. Tripe is without an exception the least economical, and the most wasteful article of consumption that the markets of this country can by possibility produce. The loss upon a pound of tripe has been found to be, in the boiling, seven-eighths of a fifth more than the loss upon a pound of any other animal substance whatever. Tripe is more expensive, properly understood, than the hot-house pineapple. Taking into account the number of animals slaughtered yearly within the bills of mortality alone; and forming a low estimate of the quantity of tripe which the carcasses of those animals, reasonably well butchered, would yield; I find that the waste on that amount of tripe, if boiled, would victual a garrison of five hundred men for five months of thirty-one days each, and a February over. The Waste, the Waste!"

Trotty stood aghast, and his legs shook under him. He seemed to have starved a garrison of five hundred men with his own hand.

"Who eats tripe?" said Mr. Filer, warmly. "Who eats tripe?"

Trotty made a miserable bow.

"You do, do you?" said Mr. Filer. "Then I'll tell you something. You snatch your tripe, my friend, out of the mouths of widows and orphans."

"I hope not, sir," said Trotty, faintly. "I'd sooner die of want!"

"Divide the amount of tripe before-mentioned, Alderman," said Filer, "by the estimated number of existing widows and orphans, and the result will be one pennyweight of tripe to each. Not a grain left for that man. Consequently, he's a robber."

CHRISTMAS BOOKS (THE CHIMES)

## SUPPER AT THE JOLLY SANDBOYS

The Jolly Sandboys was a small roadside inn of pretty ancient date, with a sign representing three Sandboys increasing their jollity with as many jugs of ale and bags of gold, creaking and swinging on its post on the opposite side of the road.

* * *

"All alone?" said Mr. Codlin, putting down his burden and wiping his forehead.

"All alone as yet," rejoined the landlord, glancing at the sky, "but we shall have more company to-night I expect. Here, one of you boys, carry that show into the barn. Make haste in out of the wet, Tom; when it came on to rain I told 'em to make the fire up, and there's a glorious blaze in the kitchen, I can tell you."

Mr. Codlin followed with a willing mind, and soon found that the landlord had not commended his preparations without good reason. A mighty fire was blazing on the hearth and roaring up the wide chimney with a cheerful sound, which a large iron cauldron, bubbling and simmering in the heat, lent its pleasant aid to swell. There was a deep, red, ruddy blush upon the room, and when the landlord stirred the fire, sending the flames skipping and leaping up —when he took off the lid of the iron pot and there rushed out a savoury smell, while the bubbling sound grew deeper and more rich, and an unctuous steam came floating out, hanging in a delicious mist above their heads—when he did this, Mr. Codlin's heart was touched.

He sat down in the chimney-corner and smiled.

Mr. Codlin sat smiling in the chimney-corner, eyeing the landlord as, with a roguish look, he held the cover in his hand, and, feigning that his doing so was needful to the welfare of the cookery, suffered the delightful steam to tickle the nostrils of his guest. The glow of the fire was upon the landlord's bald head, and upon his twinkling eye, and upon his watering mouth, and upon his pimpled face, and upon his round fat figure. Mr. Codlin drew his sleeve across his lips, and said, in a murmuring voice, "What is it?"

"It's a stew of tripe," said the landlord, smacking his lips, "and cow-heel," smacking them again, "and bacon," smacking them once more, "and steak," smacking them for the fourth time, "and peas, cauliflowers, new potatoes, and sparrow-grass, all working up together in one delicious gravy." Having come to the climax, he smacked his lips a great many times, and taking a long, hearty sniff of the fragrance that was hovering about, put on the cover again with the air of one whose toils on earth were over.

"At what time will it be ready?" asked Mr. Codlin faintly.

"It'll be done to a turn," said the landlord, looking up to the clock—and the very clock had a colour in its fat, white face, and looked a clock for Jolly Sandboys to consult—"it'll be done to a turn at twenty-two minutes before eleven."

"Then," said Mr. Codlin, "fetch me a pint of warm ale; and don't let nobody bring into the room even so much as a biscuit till the time arrives."

THE OLD CURIOSITY SHOP

## OLIVER TWIST WANTS SOME MORE

. . . A council was held; lots were cast who should walk up to the master after supper that evening, and ask for more; and it fell to Oliver Twist.

The evening arrived; the boys took their places. The master, in his cook's uniform, stationed himself at the copper; his pauper assistants ranged themselves behind him; the gruel was served out; and a long grace was said over the short commons. The gruel disappeared; the boys whispered each other, and winked at Oliver; while his next neighbours nudged him. Child as he was, he was desperate with hunger, and reckless with misery. He rose from the table; and advancing to the master, basin and spoon in hand, said: somewhat alarmed at his own temerity:

"Please, sir, I want some more."

The master was a fat, healthy man; but he turned very pale. He gazed in stupefied astonishment on the small rebel for some seconds, and then clung for support to the copper. The assistants were paralysed with wonder; the boys with fear.

"What!" said the master at length, in a faint voice.

"Please, sir," replied Oliver, "I want some more."

The master aimed a blow at Oliver's head with the ladle; pinioned him in his arms; and shrieked aloud for the beadle.

The board was sitting in solemn conclave, when Mr. Bumble rushed into the room in great excitement, and addressing the gentleman in the high chair, said,

"Mr. Limbkins, I beg your pardon, sir! Oliver Twist has asked for more!"

There was a general start. Horror was depicted on every countenance.

"For *more*!" said Mr. Limbkins. "Compose yourself, Bumble, and answer me distinctly. Do I understand that he has asked for more, after he had eaten the supper allotted by the dietary?"

"He did, sir," replied Bumble.

"The boy will be hung," said the gentleman in the white waistcoat. "I know that boy will be hung."

OLIVER TWIST

## SUPERABUNDANCE

. . . The poulterers' shops were still half open and the fruiterers' were radiant in their glory. There were great, round, pot-bellied baskets of chestnuts, shaped like the waistcoats of jolly old gentlemen, lolling at the doors, and tumbling out into the street in their apoplectic opulence. There were ruddy, brown-faced broad-girthed Spanish Onions, shining in the fatness of their growth like Spanish Friars, and winking from their shelves in wanton slyness at the girls as they went by, and glanced demurely at the hung-up mistletoe. There were pears and apples, clustered high in blooming pyramids; there were bunches of grapes, made, in the shopkeepers' benevolence to dangle from conspicuous hooks, that people's mouths might water gratis as they passed; there were piles of filberts, mossy and brown, recalling, in their fragrance, ancient walks among the woods, and pleasant shufflings ankle-deep through withered leaves; there were Norfolk Biffins, squab and swarthy, setting off the yellow of the oranges and lemons, and, in the great compactness of their juicy persons, urgently entreating and beseeching to be carried home in paper bags and eaten after dinner. . . .

The grocers'! oh, the Grocers'! nearly closed, with perhaps two shutters down, or one; but through those gaps such glimpses; it was not alone that the scales descending on the counter made a merry sound, or that the twine and roller parted company so briskly, or that the canisters were rattled up and down like juggling tricks, or even that the blended scents of tea and coffee were so grateful to the nose, or even that the raisins were so plentiful and rare, the almonds so extremely white, the sticks of cinnamon so long and straight, the other spices so delicious, the candied fruits so caked and spotted with molten sugar as to make the coldest lookers-on feel faint and subsequently bilious. Nor was it that the figs were so moist and pulpy, or that the French plums blushed in modest tartness from their highly-decorated boxes, or that everything was good to eat and in its Christmas dress; but the customers were all so hurried and so eager in the hopeful promise of the day, that they tumbled up against each other at the door, crashing their wicker baskets wildly, and left their purchases upon the counter, and came running back to fetch them, and committed hundreds of the like mistakes, in the best humour possible; while the Grocer and his people were so frank and fresh that the polished hearts with which they fastened their aprons behind might have been their own, worn outside for general inspection, and for Christmas daws to peck at if they chose.

CHRISTMAS BOOKS (A CHRISTMAS CAROL)

## THE DRY BONES OF HUNGER

And now that the cloud settled on Saint Antoine, which a momentary gleam had driven from his sacred countenance, the darkness of it was heavy—cold, dirt, sickness, ignorance, and want, were the lords in waiting on the saintly presence—nobles of great power all of them; but, most especially the last. Samples of a people that had undergone a terrible grinding and regrinding in the mill, and certainly not in the fabulous mill which ground old people young, shivered at every corner, passed in and out of every doorway, looked from every window, fluttered in every vestige of a garment that the wind shook. The mill which had worked them down, was the mill that grinds young people old; the children had ancient faces and grave voices; and upon them, and upon the grown faces, and ploughed into every furrow of age and coming up afresh, was the sign, Hunger. It was prevalent everywhere. Hunger was pushed out of the tall houses, in the wretched clothing that hung upon poles and lines; Hunger was patched into them with straw and rag and wood and paper; Hunger was repeated in every fragment of the small modicum of firewood that the man sawed off; Hunger stared down from the smokeless chimneys, and started up from the filthy street that had no offal, among its refuse, of anything to eat. Hunger was the inscription on the baker's shelves, written in every small loaf of his scanty stock of bad bread; at the sausage-shop, in every dead-dog preparation that was offered for sale. Hunger rattled its dry bones among the roasting chestnuts in the turned cylinder; Hunger was shred into atomies in every farthing porringer of husky chips of potato, fried with some reluctant drops of oil. . . . The trade signs (and they were almost as many as the shops) were, all, grim illustrations of Want. The butcher and the porkman painted up only the leanest scrags of meat; the baker, the coarsest of meagre loaves. The people rudely pictured as drinking in the wine-shops, croaked over their scanty measures of thin wine and beer, and were gloweringly confidential together. Nothing was represented in a flourishing condition, save tools and weapons; but, the cutler's knives and axes were sharp and bright, the smith's hammers heavy, and the gunsmith's stock was murderous. . . .

Across the streets at wide intervals, one clumsy lamp was slung by a rope and pulley; at night, when the lamplighter had let these down, and lighted, and hoisted them again, a feeble glow of dim wicks swung in a sickly manner overhead, as if they were at sea. Indeed they were at sea, and the ship and crew were in peril of tempest.

For the time was to come, when the gaunt scarecrows of that region should have watched the lamplighter, in their idleness and hunger, so long, as to conceive the idea of improving on his method, and hauling up men by those ropes and pulleys, to flare upon the darkness of their condition. But the time was not come yet; and every wind that blew over France shook the rags of the scarecrows in vain, for the birds, fine of song and feather, took no warning.

A TALE OF TWO CITIES

# 10

# *The Latest Hour*

## GREATER LOVE HATH NO MAN . . .

The door closed, and Carton was left alone. Straining his powers of listening to the utmost, he listened for any sound that might denote suspicion or alarm. There was none. Keys turned, doors clashed, footsteps passed along distant passages; no cry was raised, or hurry made, that seemed unusual. Breathing more freely in a little while, he sat down at the table, and listened again until the clocks struck two.

Sounds that he was not afraid of, for he divined their meaning, then began to be audible. Several doors were opened in succession, and finally his own. A jailer, with a list in his hand, looked in, merely saying, "Follow me, Evrémonde!" and he followed into a large dark room, at a distance. . . .

As he stood by the wall in a dim corner, while some of the fifty-two were brought in after him, one man stopped in passing, to embrace him, as having a knowledge of him. It thrilled him with a great dread of discovery; but the man went on.

A very few moments after that, a young woman, with a slight girlish form, a sweet spare face in which there was no vestige of colour, and large, widely-opened, patient eyes, rose from the seat where he had observed her sitting, and came to speak to him.

"Citizen Evrémonde," she said, touching him with her cold hand, "I am the poor little seamstress, who was with you in La Force."

He murmured for answer: "True. I forget what you were accused of?"

"Plots. Though the just Heaven knows I am innocent of any. Is it likely? Who would think of plotting with a poor little weak creature like me?"

The forlorn smile with which she said it, so touched him, that tears started from his eyes.

"I am not afraid to die, Citizen Evrémonde, but I have done nothing. I am not unwilling to die, if the Republic which is to do so much good to us poor, will profit by my death; but I do not know how that can be, Citizen Evrémonde. Such a poor weak little creature!"

As the last thing on earth that his heart was to warm and soften to, it warmed and softened to this pitiable girl.

"I heard you were released, Citizen Evrémonde. I hoped it was true?"

"It was. But I was again taken and condemned."

"If I may ride with you, Citizen Evrémonde, will you let me hold your hand? I am not afraid, but I am little and weak, and it will give me more courage."

As the patient eyes were lifted to his face, he saw a sudden doubt in them, and then astonishment. He pressed the work-worn, hunger-worn young fingers, and touched his lips.

"Are you dying for him?" she whispered.

"And his wife and child. Hush! Yes."

"Oh, you will let me hold your brave hand, stranger?"

"Hush! Yes, my poor sister; to the last."

* * *

Along the Paris streets, the death-carts rumble, hollow and harsh. Six tumbrils carry the day's wine to La Guillotine. All the devouring insatiable monsters imagined since imagination could record itself, are fused in the one realisation, Guillotine. And yet there is not in France, with its rich variety of soil and climate, a blade, a leaf, a root, a sprig, a peppercorn, which will grow to maturity under conditions more certain than those that have produced this horror. Crush humanity out of shape once more, under similar hammers, and it will twist itself into the same tortured forms. Sow the same seed of rapacious licence and oppression over again, and it will surely yield the same fruit according to its kind. . . .

As the sombre wheels of the six carts go round, they seem to plough up a long crooked furrow among the populace in the streets. Ridges of faces are thrown to this side and to that, and the ploughs go steadily onward. So used are the regular inhabitants of the houses to the spectacle, that in many windows there are no people, and in some the occupation of the hands is not so much as suspended, while the eyes survey the faces in the tumbrils. . . .

There is a guard of sundry horsemen riding abreast of the tumbrils, and faces are often turned up to some of them and they are asked some question. It would seem to be always the same question, for it is always followed by a press of people towards the third cart. The horsemen abreast of that cart, frequently point out one man in it with their swords. The leading curiosity is, to know which is he; he stands at the back of the tumbril with his head bent down, to converse with a mere girl who sits on the side of the cart, and holds his hand. He has no curiosity or care for the scene about him, and always speaks to the girl. Here and there in the long street of Saint Honore, cries are raised against him. If they move him at all it is only to a quiet smile, as he shakes his hair a little more loosely about his face. He cannot easily touch his face, his arms being bound. . . .

The clocks are on the stroke of three, and the furrow ploughed among the populace is turning round, to come into the place of execution, and end. The ridges thrown to this side and to that, now crumble in and close behind the last plough as it passes on, for all are following to the guillotine. In front of it, seated in chairs as in a garden of public diversion, are a number of women, busily knitting. . . .

. . . The tumbrils begin to discharge their loads.

The ministers of Saint Guillotine are robed and ready. Crash!—a head is held up, and the knitting-women who scarcely lifted their eyes to look at it a moment ago when it could think and speak, count one.

The second tumbril empties and moves on; the third comes up. Crash!—and the knitting women, never faltering or pausing in their work count two.

The supposed Evrémonde descends, and the seamstress is lifted out next after him. He has not relinquished her patient hand in getting out, but still holds it as he promised. He gently places her with her back to the crashing engine, that constantly whirrs up and falls, and she looks into his face and thanks him.

"But for you, dear stranger, I should not be so composed, for I am naturally a poor little thing, faint of heart; nor should I have been able to raise my thoughts to Him who was put to death, that we might have hope and comfort here to-day. I think you were sent to me by Heaven."

"Or you to me," says Sydney Carton. "Keep your eyes upon me, dear child, and mind no other object."

"I mind nothing while I hold your hand. I shall mind nothing when I let it go, if they are rapid."

"They will be rapid. Fear not!"

The two stand in the fast thinning throng of victims, but they speak as if they were alone. Eye to eye, voice to voice, hand to hand, heart to heart, these two children of the Universal Mother, else so wide apart and differing, have come together on the dark highway, to repair home together and to rest in her bosom. . . .

"You comfort me so much! I am so ignorant. Am I to kiss you now? Is the moment come?"

"Yes."

She kisses his lips; he kisses hers; they solemnly bless each other. The spare hand does not tremble as he releases it; nothing worse than a sweet, bright constancy is in the patient face. She goes next before him—is gone; the knitting-women count twenty-two.

"I am the Resurrection and the Life, saith the Lord: he that believeth in me, though he were dead, yet shall he live: and whosoever liveth and believeth in me, shall never die."

The murmuring of many voices, the upturning of many faces, the pressing on of many footsteps in the outskirts of the crowd, so that it swells forward in a mass, like one great heave of water, all flashes away. Twenty-three.

They said of him, about the city that night, that it was the peacefullest man's face ever beheld there. Many added that he looked sublime and prophetic.

A TALE OF TWO CITIES

## THE FUNERAL OF MRS. JOE GARGERY

It was the first time that a grave had opened in my road of life, and the gap it made in the smooth ground was wonderful. The figure of my sister in her chair by the kitchen fire haunted me night and day. That the place could possibly be without her was something my mind seemed unable to compass; and whereas she had seldom or never been in my thoughts of late, I had now the strangest idea that she was coming towards me in the street, or that she would presently knock at the door. In my rooms too, with which she had never been at all associated, there was at once the blankness of death and a perpetual suggestion of the sound of her voice or the turn of her face or figure, as if she were still alive and had been often there.

* * *

It was fine summer weather again, and, as I walked along, the times when I was a little helpless creature, and my sister did not spare me, vividly returned. But they returned with a gentle tone upon them that softened even the edge of Tickler. For now, the very breath of the beans and clover whispered to my heart that the day must come when it would be well for my memory that others walking in the sunshine should be softened as they thought of me.

At last I came within sight of the house, and saw that Trabb & Co. had put in a funereal execution and taken possession. Two dismally absurd persons, each ostentatiously exhibiting a crutch done up in a black bandage—as if that instrument could possibly communicate any comfort to anybody—were posted at the front door. . . . All the children of the village, and most of the women, were admiring these sable warders and the closed windows of the house and forge; and as I came up one of the two warders knocked at the door—implying that I was far too much exhausted by grief, to have strength remaining to knock for myself.

Another sable warder opened the door, and showed me into the best parlour. Here, Mr. Trabb had taken unto himself the best table, and had got all the leaves up, and was holding a kind of black Bazaar, with the aid of a quantity of black pins. At the moment of my arrival, he had just finished putting somebody's hat into black long clothes, like an African baby; so he held out his hand for mine. But I, misled by the action, and confused by the occasion, shook hands with him with every testimony of warm affection.

Poor dear Joe, entangled in a little black coat tied in a large bow under his chin, was seated apart at the upper end of the room; where, as chief mourner, he had evidently been stationed by Trabb. When I bent down and said to him, "Dear Joe, how are you?" he said. "Pip, old chap, you knowed her when she were a fine figure of a——" and clasped my hand and said no more.

GREAT EXPECTATIONS

## "THE OLD, OLD FASHION—DEATH!"

Paul had never risen from his little bed. He lay there, listening to the noises of the street, quite tranquilly; not caring much how the time went, but watching it and watching everything about him with observing eyes.

When the sunbeams struck into his room through the rustling blinds, and quivered on the opposite wall like golden water, he knew that evening was coming on, and that the sky was red and beautiful. As the reflection died away, and a gloom went creeping up the wall, he watched it deepen, deepen, deepen, into night. Then he thought how the long streets were dotted with lamps, and how the peaceful stars were shining overhead. His fancy had a strange tendency to wander to the river, which he knew was flowing through the great city; and now he thought how black it was, and how deep it would look, reflecting the hosts of stars—and more than all, how steadily it rolled away to meet the sea.

As it grew later in the night, and footsteps in the street become so rare that he could hear them coming, count them as they passed, and lose them in the hollow distance, he would lie and watch the many-coloured ring about the candle, and wait patiently for day. His only trouble was, the swift and rapid river. He felt forced, sometimes, to try to stop it—to stem it with his childish hands—or choke its way with sand—and when he saw it coming on, resistless, he cried out! But a word from Florence, who was always at his side, restored him to himself; and leaning his poor head upon her breast, he told Floy of his dream, and smiled.

When day began to dawn again, he watched for the sun; and when its cheerful light began to sparkle in the room, he pictured to himself—pictured! he saw the high church towers rising up into the morning sky, the town reviving, waking, starting into life once more, the river glistening as it rolled (but rolling fast as ever), and the country bright with dew. Familiar sounds and cries came by degrees into the street below; the servants in the house were roused and busy; faces looked in at the door, and voices asked his attendants softly how he was. Paul always answered for himself, "I am better, I am a great deal better, thank you! Tell Papa so!"

By little and little, he got tired of the bustle of the day, the noise of carriages and carts, and people passing and repassing, and would fall asleep, or be troubled with a restless and uneasy sense again—the child could hardly tell whether this were in his sleeping or his waking moments—of that rushing river. "Why will it never stop, Floy?" he would sometimes ask her. "It is bearing me away, I think?"

But Floy could always soothe and reassure him; and it was his daily delight to make her lay her head down on his pillow and take some rest.

* * *

"Now lay me down," he said, "and, Floy, come close to me, and let me see you!"

Sister and brother wound their arms around each other, and the golden light came streaming in, and fell upon them, locked together.

"How fast the river runs, between its green banks and the rushes, Floy! But it's very near the sea. I hear the waves! They always said so!"

Presently he told her that the motion of the boat upon the stream was lulling him to rest. How green the banks were now, how bright the flowers growing on them, and how tall the rushes! Now the boat was out at sea, but gliding smoothly on. And now there was a shore before him. Who stood on the bank!—

He put his hands together, as he had been used to do at his prayers. He did not remove his arms to do it; but they saw him fold them so, behind her neck.

"Mama is like you, Floy. I know her by the face! But tell them that the print upon the stairs at school is not divine enough. The light about the head is shining on me as I go!"

The golden ripple on the wall came back again, and nothing else stirred in the room. The old, old fashion! The fashion that came in with our first garments, and will last unchanged until our race has run its course, and the wide firmament is rolled up like a scroll. The old, old fashion—Death!

DOMBEY AND SON

# 11

# *The Aphorisms of Samuel and Tony Weller*

## *from* PICKWICK PAPERS

"You're one o' the adwice gratis order," thought Sam, "or you wouldn't be so werry fond o' me all at once."

"What the devil do you want with me, as the man said wen he see the ghost?"

"That's the pint, sir," interposed Sam; "Out vith it, as the father said to the child, wen he swallowed a farden."

"There's a change of air, plenty to see, and little to do; and all this suits my complaint uncommon."

"He wants you partickler; and no one else'll do, as the devil's private secretary said ven he fetched avay Doctor Faustus."

"Here's your servant, sir. Proud o' the title, as the living skellinton said, ven they show'd him."

"There's nothin' so refreshin' as sleep, sir, as the servant-girl said afore she drank the egg-cupful o' laudanum."

"Battledore and shuttlecock's a wery good game vhen you ain't the shuttlecock and two lawyers the battledores, in which case it gets too excitin' to be pleasant."

"The gout is a complaint as arises from too much ease and comfort. If ever you're attacked with the gout, sir, jist you marry a widder as has got a good loud woice, with a decent notion of usin' it, and you'll never have the gout agin. It's a capital prescription, sir. I takes it reg'lar, and I can warrant it to drive away any illness as is caused by two much jollity."

"I think he's the wictim o' connubiality, as Blue Beard's domestic chaplain said, vith a tear of pity, ven he buried him."

"Widders are 'ceptions to ev'ry rule. I *have* heerd how many ord'nary women one widder's equal to in pint o' comin' over you. I think it's five-and-twenty, but I don't rightly know vether it ain't more."

"Coaches, Sammy, is like guns—they requires to be loaded with wery great care, afore they go off."

"If ever you gets to up'ards o' fifty, and feels disposed to go a marryin' anybody—no matter who—jist you shut yourself up in your own room, if you've got one, and pison yourself off hand. Hangin's wulgar, so don't you have nothin' to say to that. Pison yourself, Samivel, my boy, pison yourself, and you'll be glad on it arterwards."

"This is a wery impartial country for justice," said Sam. "There ain't a magistrate goin' as don't commit himself twice as often as he commits other people."

"All good feelin', sir—the wery best intentions, as the gen'l'm'n said wen he run away from his wife 'cos she seemed unhappy with him."

"Ven you're a married man, Samivel, you'll understand a good many things as you don't understand now; but vether it's vorth while goin' through so much, to learn so little, as the charity-boy said ven he got to the end of the alphabet, is a matter o' taste. *I* rayther think it isn't."

". . . vich I call addin' insult to injury, as the parrot said ven they not only took him from his native land, but made him talk the English langwidge arterwards."

"I think I see your drift; and if I do see your drift, it's my 'pinion that you're comin' it a great deal too strong, as the mail-coachman said to the snowstorm, ven it overtook him."

"Anythin' for a quiet life, as the man said wen he took the sitivation at the lighthouse."

"He's a ma-licious, bad-disposed, vordly-minded, spiteful, windictive creetur, with a hard heart as there ain't no soft'nin as the wirtuous clergyman remarked of the old gen'l'm'n with the dropsy, ven he said, that upon the whole he thought he'd rayther leave his property to his vife than build a chapel vith it."

"Avay with melincholly, as the little boy said ven his school-missis died."

"This is rayther a change for the worse, as the gen'l'm'n said, wen he got two doubtful shillin's and sixpenn'orth o' pocket-pieces for a good half-crown."

"I only assisted natur', ma'am; as the doctor said to the boy's mother, arter he'd bled him to death."

"You'll find that as you get vider, you'll get viser. Vidth and visdom, Sammy, alvays grows together."